STU ✓

The Story of Nine Inventors

TRAIL BLAZERS
OF TECHNOLOGY

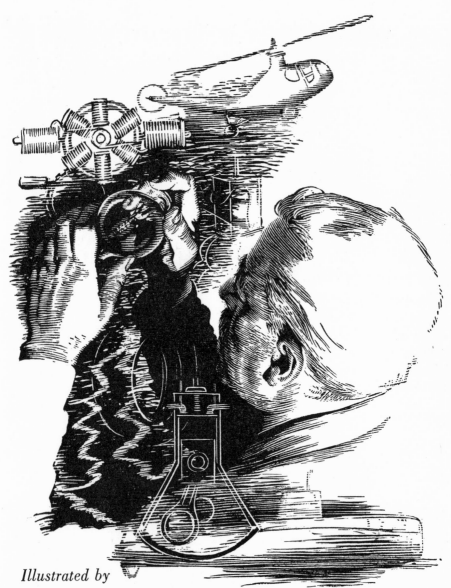

Illustrated by
Anthony Ravielli

TRAIL BLAZERS
OF TECHNOLOGY
The Story of Nine Inventors

by HARLAND MANCHESTER

CHARLES SCRIBNER'S SONS *New York*

This book is dedicated to the patient wives of men who are obsessed with Ideas, with the consoling thought that without men like their husbands we would all be living in caves.

The author gratefully thanks the editors of *The Reader's Digest* for their appreciation of these biographical sketches, most of which appeared in the *Digest* in their original form, and for their kind permission to use material from the sketches in this book.

FOREWORD

This book is the story of nine men who possessed the rare gift of invention. Invention, Webster tells us, is "the power to conceive and present new combinations of facts or ideas, to devise new methods or instruments." Many people have this power to some degree, but fail to perceive the potential impact of their discoveries upon the life of man. These nine men had prophetic vision which enabled them to project their often unimpressive pioneer devices upon the great screen of today's technological complex. While literature teems with similar forecasts by farseeing men who were content with idle speculation, these inventors were possessed by a third essential

1

quality: a vital power which overrode all doubts and obstacles —a fierce, impatient compulsion to force their ideas upon a reluctant world. Armed with this remarkable combination of personal traits, they did much to create the world we live in. No person in the cities, villages and farms of the civilized world can now spend a routine day without the aid of some of the machines and systems which first took form in their restless, intuitive minds.

These inventors differed widely in racial, educational and social background. Few of them could be called "well-rounded." Most of them were prickly individualists—"inner-directed" men who were deaf to group opinion and stubbornly adhered to their private convictions. None of them would fit into a modern industrial research laboratory, or would be happy in the group social life expected of their modern counterparts. Many of them were permanently scarred by their early discovery that society grimly resists change. Somewhat as the mechanisms of the human body work to preserve uniform conditions, industry and consumers tend to reject radical innovations. Such conservatism is doubtless valuable in protecting society against the whims of visionaries, but it culls the crop of new ideas ruthlessly, not always fairly, and often delays the adoption of useful inventions so long that the true creators do not profit from their work.

These pioneers were all citizens of the nineteenth century. Most of them did their main work in that period; all were inspired by its educational systems and social philosophy. There has been much discussion of the changing role of the inventor since their time. What would be the lot of such individualists if they were starting their careers today? There have been many speculations by prominent educators and scientists.

"Today the typical lone inventor of the eighteenth and nineteenth century has all but disappeared," says Dr. James Bryant Conant, president emeritus of Harvard University. "In his place in the mid-twentieth century came the industrial research laboratory and departments of development engineering."

Writes John Kenneth Galbraith, noted economist, in his book *American Capitalism:* "A benign Providence . . . has made the modern industry of a few large firms an almost perfect instrument for inducing technical change . . . There is no more pleasant fiction than that technical change is the product of the matchless ingenuity of the small man forced by competition to employ his wits to better his neighbors . . . Technical development has long since become the preserve of the scientist and the engineer. Most of the cheap and simple inventions have, to put it bluntly, been made."

Engineers at the Bell Telephone Laboratories, birthplace of the transistor, which has now largely supplanted Lee de Forest's audion tube for many uses, state that it would have been impossible for even a genius of de Forest's stature to develop this superior new device with the meager equipment and technical assistance at his disposal. The revolutionary audion tube, the basis of radio, television and a thousand other devices of the electronics age, was inexpensively built by a small fabricator of Christmas-tree bulbs under the direction of the inventor. The transistor, whose inventors won the Nobel

Prize in physics, required a heavy research investment, the aid of many skilled scientists, and the use of complicated and expensive instruments which are not available to most individual inventors.

"Yet even the best-equipped laboratory can only provide suitable working conditions and the intellectual stimulation of gifted colleagues," comments one Bell scientist. "Without a constant invasion of new young individualists fired by the spark of creativity, our laboratories would be sterile."

Dr. John R. Dunning, nuclear physicist and dean of the Columbia University School of Engineering and Applied Science, points out that in a period of huge government-financed research projects we must place high value upon individual thinking. "Our best geniuses use only about ten per cent of their talent," he says. "Our school system sometimes beats the geniuses into line and discourages original ideas. A good man will survive almost any system, but we must create an environment in which he will become more prolific, for individual initiative is a priceless key to our effectiveness as a nation."

Asked what are the chances of the lone inventor today, Dr. Vannevar Bush, director of the Office of Scientific Research and Development in World War II, replied:

"There never was a 'lone' inventor. Behind every great invention there were many men who made essential contributions and received little public credit. There have been, of course, starving inventors. I have seen many men wreck their lives in inventing when with a little better planning they might have achieved notable success. Cooperative work yields faster results. Today, inventions great and small are constantly being made in the big scientific laboratories.

"My advice to the young man of today who has a big idea is, first of all, get a good technical education. Next, get a job in a well-equipped research laboratory. There he will learn the complicated techniques of modern research, exchange ideas with colleagues, and learn how money is spent in new developments. Then, if his plan still looks good, it is time to think about securing capital and setting out on his own. At least a dozen young men in my wartime research group went out to form their own companies and have made a go of it."

While members of research organizations speak highly of cooperative effort, other innovators who have set out alone are sharply critical of their attitude. Edwin H. Land, who left Harvard to set up a small basement laboratory which grew into the Polaroid Corporation, and whose many inventions include the versatile light-polarizing film and the well-known camera, commented in a paper in the *Harvard Business Review* that while human beings in the mass are fun at square dances and football games, "there is no such thing as group originality or group creativity or group perspicacity.

"Teams are not creative as such," he continued. "For every good idea that has been spawned by a group, millions have been smothered . . . We see the world spending billions of dollars on group research and group invention all over the world for an output that I predict will in retrospect seem scandalously limited with relation to the size of the investment . . .

"Every significant step is taken by some individual who has freed himself from a way of thinking that is held by friends and associates who may be more intelligent, better educated, better disciplined, but who have not mastered the art of the fresh, clean look at the old, old knowledge."

However the role of the inventor may have changed since the days of Charles Goodyear and Thomas Davenport, there is a greater demand today than ever before in the world's history for original methods of solving problems. Every important invention creates the need for many more inventions to adapt it to human needs. The automobile created a demand for traffic control systems, clover-leaf intersections, highway radar, automatic gasoline pumps, automatic garages, motels, numbered highway systems, seat belts, road maps and a long list of other new devices and concepts which have often required as much ingenuity as the machine that spawned them. By taking over much of the task once performed by public transportation, the automobile has created an acute need for new inventions in urban rapid transit, railroads and other common carriers, to enable them to regain their lost functions with great savings to the public. Alert young inventors aware of public needs may some day make our present transportation jumble seem as antiquated as the stagecoach.

Our constantly changing environment creates a continuous demand for new inventions. The decline of household labor and the increase in the number of career women offer a bonanza to any inventor who can make it easier and cheaper to maintain houses, clean garments, prepare meals and care for children. The prolongation of life by new drugs and medical techniques offers great rewards for anyone who can invent devices and methods which will make old age more profitable and enjoyable.

A list of projects which demand the attention of today's inventors would include the following: more efficient utilization of water supplies; river purification; cheaper methods of highway snow removal; smog abatement; new vehicles for crossing rough terrain; new methods of house heating; noise abatement; an economic method for the utilization of solar energy; methods for the economic utilization of farm and forest wastes; methods of curbing insect pests without poisoning birds and fish; a practical vertical-take-off high-speed air vehicle; dwarf lawn grass that needs no mowing; glareless highway illumination; and better utilization of worn-out automobiles and other machines.

Unknown inventors who need advice now have a useful ally in the National Inventors Council, an agency of the Department of Commerce in Washington, D. C. Organized in 1940 to evaluate unsolicited inventions which might be of use to the military services, the Council has screened thousands of ideas, many of which have been adopted. The Council publishes frequent lists of inventions wanted by the armed forces and other government agencies, which it will send to any interested person.

Many useful inventions are not mechanical devices, but "social inventions" which require equal originality and daring. Among them are the chain store, the mail order company, the supermarket, the consumers' cooperative, the trade union, the Department of Agriculture's county agent system, the

Great Books Clubs, the correspondence course, installment buying and the telephone-answering service. All these inventions were once privately visualized by one or more individualists who saw things differently than did their neighbors and who were doubtless told that their plans were impractical. Today we need social inventors more than ever, for our technology has far outrun our ability to utilize it in the best interests of humanity. Social inventors who are now in grade school may conceive new ways to improve our educational system, halt the decline of our cities, reduce crime, ease prejudices, and promote world peace. A study of the lives of great inventors shows that it is not too early for them to start thinking about such problems.

Innovators will all be chided for their folly by well-meaning people who will tell them, quite rightly, that security and serenity can better be attained by following beaten paths. None of these warnings will stop the man who is obsessed with an invention, any more than statistics about the income of the average writer or artist can stop a man from writing a book or painting a picture. There will always be adventurous innovators, who in the teeth of discouragement and adversity will plight their careers to courageous quests. Many of their star-hitched wagons will collapse on the trail. Many pioneers will sow to see others reap. A few will win fortune and fame. All must know, as they set forth on their pilgrimages, that the unique joys of experimentation and creation will be their greatest reward.

H. M.

CONTENTS

The Story of Nine Inventors

TRAIL BLAZERS
OF TECHNOLOGY

CHAPTER ONE

THOMAS DAVENPORT

The Brandon Blacksmith

On a December day of 1833, Thomas Davenport, a young blacksmith of Brandon, Vermont, set out with his brother Oliver on a twenty-five-mile wagon trip to Crown Point, just beyond the New York line. Thomas had heard that in a Crown Point iron works there was a "wonderful galvanic battery," which would "suspend an anvil between heaven and earth," which would "suspend an anvil between heaven and earth."

He had persuaded his brother, a tin peddler, to drive him there, and they jolted over frozen ruts to the clatter of pots and pans. They came to Otter Creek, which had no bridge. As Oliver urged his skittish young horse onto the ice, he saw a large crack in the middle of the stream. That ended the expedition, he said; they would have to turn back. Thomas shook his head—a powerful, prow-like head mounted on a slight, wiry body.

"No, we can't go back," he said. "Jump the horse over." Oliver stared at his brother. Then he jumped the horse over the crack. Thomas was right. He could never go back, and neither he nor the world were ever quite the same again.

Thomas Davenport was a very determined man. Later he was to be called stubborn, foolhardy, and even slightly crazy. Once before he had made the tedious trip to see the marvelous device, but the proprietors were away and he was disappointed. Someone had told him that a man in Albany had constructed the machine, so he made his way to Albany, to him a confusing metropolis. He asked a rooming-house keeper where he could find the "galvanic battery." The puzzled landlord sent him to a tinsmith, the tinsmith thought that maybe jewelers used something of the kind, and a jeweler suggested that he go to a foundry. He finally postponed the quest and returned to his forge, weary and footsore. He had no horse of his own, and there was no railroad.

On this trip he was successful. It was getting dark when the brothers reached Crown Point, but the iron works were open, and at last Davenport stood before the mysterious device which had kept his mind in a turmoil. It was the electromagnet invented a few years before by Professor Joseph Henry of Albany and Princeton. Suspended from a kind of gallows, the height of a man, was a piece of soft iron which had been forged in the shape of a horseshoe about a foot long. Wound tightly around the horseshoe was a coil of silk-insulated copper wire.

The ends of the wire were connected to the zinc and copper plates of a simple wet battery to furnish power.

Professor Henry was a pioneer in his field, and there were only a few electromagnets in existence. The one at Crown Point was probably the most powerful in the world, so powerful that it would suspend heavy chunks of metal beneath it. The iron works people sometimes made it perform this theatrical trick for spectators, but they had purchased it for a practical reason. To separate the iron from the waste in the low-grade ore then mined in the region, they used a sorter fitted with small permanent magnets. When these permanent magnets lost their power, Henry's electromagnet provided a quick method of replenishing it.

It was Saturday night in the town, and a number of bystanders joined the brothers to gaze at the magical instrument. The mill operators put it through its paces, and Davenport saw with his own eyes that it would actually hold a small anvil in the air by some mysterious means. He knew nothing about magnetism, but his arms knew the weight of an anvil. He turned pale with excitement in the presence of the miracle. Ordinarily taciturn, he now burst forth with a volley of questions. He had no idea what words to use. He called the batteries "cups," and the magnet a "battery." If you cut a wire leading to the cups, would the weight drop, he wanted to know. They told him it would. He brashly asked permission to cut one of the wires to prove it, and was curtly refused. How much did the horseshoe weigh? Three pounds. And the block of iron? A hundred and fifty pounds.

"Here was one of the wonders of Nature and Providence,"

he wrote later. "Like a flash of lightning the thought occurred to me, that here was an available power within the reach of man. If three pounds of iron and copper wire would suspend in the air one hundred and fifty pounds, what would three hundred pounds suspend?"

Suddenly eloquent, Davenport proclaimed to the startled group that this new power must be put to work, that ships would be propelled with it, that "the red lightning of heaven would be tamed" and become the servant of mankind.

The strollers stared at him uneasily. He turned to the operators and asked the price of the apparatus. They said they would sell it for seventy-five dollars, which was probably more than Davenport had ever owned in ready cash. He had brought a little money to buy supplies for his shop, but now the shop was forgotten. He proposed to Oliver that they drive the tin wagon to the center of town and hold a public auction to raise the balance of the sum. Oliver reluctantly consented.

They took up their stand and Oliver limbered his lungs in the jargon of the Vermont auctioneer. For a time the buckets and dust pans sold briskly, but Thomas soon concluded that the sum couldn't be raised that way. While Oliver was busy with his sales patter, Thomas unhitched the horse and led him away. After a quick trade he returned with a miserable wreck of an animal, and money to boot, which brought their total resources to seventy-five dollars.

When he had paid over the money, Thomas performed his first experiment. He whipped out his pocketknife, cut one of the battery wires, and proved to himself that the magnet had lost its power. Then he held the severed ends of wire together and found that it would once more lift weights. To-day, everyone who completes a circuit by turning a switch repeats Davenport's experiment, but in 1833 there were only a few men in the world who knew what would happen.

The brothers loaded the equipment into the cart and started on the long journey back to Brandon. Oliver was hungry and disheartened. They wouldn't even be able to buy dinner on the way home.

"Never mind," said Thomas. "Maybe we shan't want any."

It was late at night when the horse finally halted before the blacksmith's house. Thomas dashed in with his precious mag-net, aroused Emily, his wife, and asked her to bring pen and paper. Then he began to unwind the wire from the soft-iron horseshoe. Aghast, Oliver pleaded with him not to destroy it. They could show it in a hall and charge admission, he said.

"No," said Thomas impatiently, "I'm going to find out how it's built, so I can make another."

As excited as her husband, Emily copied down, as Thomas recited them, the number of turns of wire and the minutest details of the magnet's construction. When the device was completely dismantled and the description written down, Thomas rose from the table, haggard but triumphant. Dupli-cating Henry's magnet was only the first point of his program. He was looking far ahead. Here was power in the raw—power that would move mountains. He was determined to build what he called an electromagnetic engine if the job killed him. It did.

From that day on, Thomas Davenport was a man possessed. His deepset eyes grew prophetic, his face hectic and consecrated. Farmers found him too busy to shoe their horses and oxen, and departed, muttering, to his competitors. Word got about that Tom Davenport was working on a "perpetual motion machine"—a type of mechanically impossible engine, proposed by many amateurs, which was intended to run without fuel or outside power. Small children stared at him, and Emily's practical father lectured him.

From any sensible point of view, his conduct was utter folly. He had mastered a sound calling, and business at the shop was fair enough. He had built a good brick house and had a devoted wife and two fine sons. He had every reason to expect a serene life of modest security. He had all the more reason to cling to his station because he had won it after a grim ordeal of drudgery and poverty, for he had started life far behind scratch.

Thomas Davenport was born in 1802 on a stony mountain farm near Williamstown, Vermont, fifty miles north of Brandon. He was the seventh of ten children. When he was ten years old, his father died, and he began doing a man's work, which meant hard labor from dawn to dusk with crude hand implements. He never played. When his mother could spare him between seasonal periods of harvest, planting and wood chopping, he sometimes spent a few weeks in an overcrowded, one-room school. He was extremely shy, and slow and awkward of speech. When the bell rang for recess, he remained at his desk reading. His brother recalled that when he was stuck by a problem in arithmetic, he stubbornly refused help, and fought it out by himself. The total of this schooling, seized in intermittent snatches, could not have

amounted to more than three years. Later he took books from
the tiny village library, but none of them informed him of
the progress of science, or "natural philosophy," as scholars
then called it.

When he was fourteen, his mother surrendered to the rocks
and weeds and gave up the farm, and the family was broken
up. Thomas became a bound-out apprentice to Thomas Abbott
and Enoch Howe, thrifty, pious blacksmiths who ran a shop
in Williamstown. Under the law he was required to serve his
masters without pay until he was twenty-one, in return for
which they were to feed and clothe him, teach him the "art,
trade or mystery" of blacksmithing, and give him two suits
when the seven years had expired, one for working and one
for Sundays. No spending money and no holidays were
stipulated. His masters found him diligent and dutiful, but
told the neighbors that he "worked too much with his head"
to make a really good blacksmith, that "he had too many
things in his mind, and . . . was afraid he would never
amount to much." He had an unfortunate habit of stoking the
forge with one hand while he held a book in the other. Somewhere he found a fragment of a book about the "wonders of
science," and this was his favorite. And he had a fife which an
older brother had carried in the War of 1812. Sometimes he
played it in the evening.

When his term of apprenticeship was over, Thomas took
his two suits and crossed the Green Mountain Divide to
Brandon, where his brother Barzilla was established as a
lawyer. He opened his own smithy on credit, thrived, married,
built his house and "settled down." For ten years he worked

at his forge, and then rumors came over the hills about Henry's "galvanic battery."

The morning after he returned to Brandon with his treasure, Davenport went to his shop and began the construction of a soft-iron horseshoe many times larger than the original. When it was done, Emily helped him wind it according to the directions she had put down. Then he set about inventing a motor, with all the confidence he would have had in shoeing an unruly horse. He had never talked with an inventor, a scientist or an engineer, and there was no one in his little world who understood what he was about.

Michael Faraday, the eminent English scientist, had stated years before that a rotary electric motor might sometime be invented, and a number of experimenters in America and Europe had constructed magnetic toys which would vibrate delicate pendulums or set small bells tinkling. Davenport had not even heard the names of these men and would not have been interested in their puny gadgets. He was building a motor, he said, that would run machinery, ships and railroad trains, and he was wasting no time about it.

His approach was simple and direct. He had a machine that would exert power in a straight line, and he was going to make that power move continuously in a circle. The unknown ancient who took a sled runner and bent it into a wheel, the men who conceived the turbine, the rotary press, and such devices as rotary butter churns and washing machines were all moved by the same instinctive impulse—bend a straight line into a circle and things go faster and easier.

Davenport's first step was to drill a hole in the center of a straight, magnetized bar and mount it on a pin at its exact center of gravity. Then he set up his electromagnet near it. The bar spun around like the needle of a compass and stopped short when its negative pole was opposite the positive pole of the electromagnet. He thought that if he could break the current quickly enough before the bar stopped rotating, its momentum would carry it around in a circle until its pole came again within the pull of the electromagnet. Then it would receive another kick to keep it going.

He and Emily spent long hours trying to make the balanced magnet do this trick. It looked simple enough to them, but they could not break the current by hand quickly enough to prevent the bar from stopping.

"It's no use," said Thomas, in a rare moment of despair. "There is no power short of the Almighty quick enough to do that."

Emily urged him not to give up. Trying everything they could think of, they rediscovered a method which had been used in laboratories for quickly breaking an electric circuit —the use of mercury as a conductor. They dipped the two wires leading from the electromagnet into small cups of mercury, which were connected with the battery. Now they could turn off the power almost instantaneously by jerking one of the wires out of its cup. Timing the movement properly took long practice. Finally, at three o'clock one morning, they succeeded in making the magnetized bar go round and round on its pivot. Davenport had proved his point—that if this "galvanic battery" could lift an anvil, it could be made to turn a wheel. Greatly encouraged, he set about making a practical motor, firmly believing that within a few years this new power would displace the steam engine.

He gained an ally in a twenty-two-year-old blacksmith and wheelwright named Orange Smalley, who had a shop near his. Smalley's curiosity had been aroused by a scientific lecture he had once heard at a country schoolhouse, and while other townsmen joked about Davenport's crazy notions, Smalley went to his shop and listened with mounting excitement to his plans for revolutionizing the world's power. To him this was simply another job, like building a new kind of wagon. He came to help Davenport, and offered his savings for the purchase of materials. They set to work on a device that would eliminate the necessity of breaking the circuit by hand—a device known today as a "commutator." It automatically reversed the positions of the wires in the mercury cups, thus reversing the current in the electromagnet with each revolution of the revolving bar. This greatly added to its speed and power. They made constant improvements and constructed a number of motors.

In July, 1834, seven months after his first introduction to the subject of electricity, Thomas Davenport had built an electric motor out of intuition and scraps. It had four electromagnets. Two, mounted on a wheel, took the place of the revolving bar of steel, and two stationary magnets stood opposite each other outside the wheel. Their makeshift commutator reversed the curent with each half-turn of the wheel, which traveled steadily at thirty revolutions a minute. It was still a crude and feeble machine, but in principle it was the father of every direct-current electric motor in the world today.

Davenport jubilantly called in his neighbors to show them that he was no hare-brained putterer with perpetual motion schemes. He had been sensitive about their gossip, and now he would set them right about his wonderful plan for universal power. They came and looked at the slowly moving wheel. They listened in silence while he haltingly explained that this was no attempt at *perpetual* motion, a clearly impossible goal, but rather *magnetic* motion, based on principles which he had proved. It was true, he admitted, that this little engine was only strong enough to raise a few ounces one foot high every minute, but the principle was what mattered. By making larger electromagnets and mounting a dozen of them on the revolving wheel instead of two, the power could be increased enormously. With a little time and money, he declared earnestly, he could build engines that would drive trains or anything else.

Davenport might as well have said that he was building a rocket ship, for he saw nothing but frozen faces and ill-concealed smiles. The town wit announced that the "perpetual motion man" had produced a "mosquito-power engine." The only encouragement came from a farmer who promised Davenport a hundred dollars if he would build an engine that would run his grindstone. This was no help, for without the money in advance, he could not build the engine.

Casting about for someone who would take him at face value, Davenport approached Brandon's one acknowledged intellectual, the village pastor. The minister listened patiently and delivered the tight-lipped opinion that if the machine were good for anything, it would have been in use long before. A blacksmith, he intimated, should stick to his forge.

Then Davenport thought of the universities. He had never seen a college or met a professor, and like many unschooled men, he held them in great awe. Middlebury College was twenty miles north of Brandon, and on a cold, stormy day he and Smalley loaded the motor on a cart and made the trip. They set up the machine in a room at the village tavern, and Davenport, screwing up his courage, sought out Professor Edward Turner, teacher of natural philosophy. Once assured that Davenport was no "perpetual motion man," Turner saw a demonstration of the motor and was keenly interested.

"What you have invented is nothing less than a new motive power," he pronounced. He sent for a colleague, Professor William C. Fowler, who declared that the motor would turn out to be "one of the greatest inventions of the nineteenth century." Turner agreed that such motors might well propel trains and boats. He wrote a letter of introduction to his friend Professor Amos Eaton of Rensselaer Institute, explained the business of obtaining a patent, and recommended a book in which Davenport could find the correct names of the instruments and materials he had been using.

Elated at this meeting with his peers, Davenport went home and showed his letters to the skeptics. He decided to build a better engine before presenting Turner's letter. Taking apart his older motors to get materials, he built a faster, stronger one with twelve electromagnets in the revolving wheel. This increased the motor's speed to a point where his crude, mercury-cup commutator would no longer reverse the current fast enough, so he hammered the contact wires into thin springs and attached them so that they rubbed against the shaft of the wheel. When segments of the shaft were insulated, the wires reversed the current periodically, thus providing the positive and negative impulses which kept the wheel spinning. This was the origin of the "brush commutator" now universally used.

By this time, cash and credit were running low. Smalley got discouraged, withdrew from the venture, and returned to his trade. Davenport found another partner in a mechanic named Richardson. Tearing down old motors, they made a dozen new ones, slowly working out a more efficient design. Then the new partner left, and Davenport worked on alone. He was anxious to secure his patent, but that meant a long and expensive trip to Washington. Davenport canvassed his neighbors, and now six of them were sufficiently impressed to make up a purse for the journey.

Armed with his letter from Turner and a note from his congressman, Davenport went first to Troy, New York, where Professor Eaton of Rensselaer immediately became his champion. Eaton sent him to Princeton to see Professor Henry, inventor of the electromagnet. Henry, enthusiastic, sent him to Philadelphia, where his motor was exhibited at the Franklin Institute. It was something of a tour of triumph, but by the time Davenport reached Washington these side excursions had

depleted his funds. If he paid the patent fee, he would be un-
able to pay his fare home. So he bought a ticket back to Troy,
and arrived at Eaton's house without a cent.

He asked Eaton if Rensselaer Institute wouldn't buy his
motor so that he could get home; he would sell it for thirty
dollars. Eaton gave him a note to General Van Rensselaer,
founder and patron of the Institute, urging him to make the
purchase, and Davenport hurried to Van Rensselaer's house.

As he entered the gate, the General's three large watchdogs
fell upon him and tore his clothes to ribbons. The General and
two servants pulled the dogs off, and while a maid knelt beside him tacking his suit together, Davenport tried to explain
his invention. He got his thirty dollars and left for Brandon.
This was probably the world's first sale of an electric motor,
but he came home without his patent, and with little left of
his pants.

For two years he had worked day and night on his invention,
and now he was utterly discouraged. He was destitute, his
neighbors had completely lost faith in him, and his wife and
children were struggling along on next to nothing. His father-
in-law offered him every inducement to give up his mad
scheme and relight the fire in his forge, and the heartsick man
admitted that he was right.

But Davenport had started something that could not be
stopped. Professor Eaton, staking his reputation on the motor,
had written an article about it which was widely copied by
the press, and several men had pledged money to help the
inventor. Professor Benjamin Silliman of Yale, one of the
country's leading scientific authorities, had prepared an en-

thusiastic paper for his *Journal*. Then a skeptical article appeared in a New York paper which was a slap in the face to the learned men who had lent their names to Davenport's project. Professor Eaton took up the challenge, and without consulting Davenport, announced that the Brandon blacksmith would give a free demonstration of his motor in the Troy courthouse on October 14, 1835—a date only a few weeks away.

"This will give you a chance to exhibit truth," he wrote to Davenport. "I tell you *truth*—TRUTH is everything!"

Davenport penned an anguished refusal, telling Eaton of his plight and his new resolution. He couldn't even buy materials to build a new motor, he explained.

Eaton brushed aside all objections.

"Make my name Thomas Davenport," he wrote, "and I will give you five thousand dollars for your idea. . . . It is a thing which will progress slowly; perhaps it may never yield you anything but reputation. But you have involved friends; and it is your duty to support their pledges for you. . . . Remember, if you fail to be here on the fourteenth, destruction is your portion!"

Eaton followed up his letter by buying all the copper wire to be found in Albany and sending it to Brandon by stagecoach. Davenport wavered. Eaton's rhetoric would not feed his family. He told his wife that the plan was impossible, for he couldn't buy the silk which he had been led to believe was the only material suitable for insulating the wires.

Emily silently disappeared and returned with her one treasure, her silk wedding dress. That settled the matter. To-

gether they tore the dress into strips and wound the wires of
the new motor.

The exhibition in Troy vindicated the professors. It brought
applause from hundreds of spectators, but no money to the
inventor. One of the onlookers, a young mechanic of Cabots-
ville, near Springfield, Massachusetts, asked Davenport to go
home with him and work in his shop. The two men built a
model of a circular electric railway three feet in diameter.
The power house stood in the center, and a miniature locomotive sped around the track. When it was finished, his partner
was in no position to go further with the venture. Once more
Davenport was alone and without funds. It was the middle of
December, and he was a hundred and fifty miles from home.

"Pennyless though I was," he wrote later, "I could not
bear the thought that I should never make further improvements in the application of electromagnetic power."

His only potential asset was a businesslike letter from a
Dedham manufacturer of textile machinery, who asked him
to bring his motor for a trial. A good samaritan named Kimball, who hardly knew Davenport, advanced fifty dollars for
the trip. Still wearing his dog-mangled suit, the inventor took
his engine to Dedham in high expectation. Unimpressed, the
manufacturer dismissed him coolly, without even paying the
expenses of the trip. In an attempt to raise money to repay
Kimball, Davenport went on to Boston and set up his motor
in a hotel room, hoping "that the thinking portion of that
intelligent city would be highly gratified with an exhibition."
A few people came and saw a frail, tattered fanatic whose
talk they couldn't follow. The only enthusiast was a small

boy named Thomas Hall, who made sketches of the device, and long after Davenport's death became a successful manufacturer of electrical equipment. Otherwise, the passage through Boston left no ripple.

Kimball came to the rescue again. He took the dejected man into his home for a few weeks and bought him a new suit. Then the faithful Oliver appeared with the old tin wagon and took Thomas and his models back to the safe haven of Brandon.

By this time there was no question of Davenport's returning to his trade. He had burned his bridges, and his life depended on his motor. He tried to support his family by giving exhibitions. Observing that people seemed "worn out and tired" of his talk, he hired an eloquent Vermonter named Johnnie Thompson to make the speeches. The act had a good two weeks' run at Saratoga. There he met Ransom Cook, a leading citizen and prosperous manufacturer, and his fortunes suddenly improved.

Inspired by Davenport's dream of power, Cook closed down his busy factory, and with the help of his mechanics the two men set happily to work building new electric motors. For the second time the inventor went to Washington to apply for his patent, this time with his mind at ease and ample funds in his pocket. But disaster followed him. The patent office burned down, and the model and description went up in flames. The partners immediately built another model, and Davenport's third trip was successful. Early in 1837 he obtained the world's first patent on an electric motor. The patent broadly covered the use of "magnetic and electromagnetic power as a moving principle for machinery in the manner above de-

scribed, or in any other substantially the same in principle."
If this patent were in force today, its owner's wealth would
be too fantastic to reckon.

Dazzling publicity followed. Newspapers predicted, half
a century too early, a revolution in industry and transportation. Professor Silliman examined the motor and exclaimed
that "nothing since the discovery of gravitation and of the
structure of the celestial systems is so wonderful as the power
evolved by galvanism." There is a legend that Davenport
refused an offer of forty thousand dollars for his interest in
the invention.

His partner, however, had made other plans to hasten the
revolution of power. While Davenport was in Washington, a
New York promoter interested Cook in a rosy stock-selling
scheme, promising the partners an initial payment of twelve
thousand dollars within thirty days. They moved their workshop to New York, where the *Herald* promptly hailed the
"Dawn of a New Civilization" and proclaimed the invention
"the greatest of ancient and modern times, the greatest the
world has ever seen, the greatest the world will ever see. . . ."
And the *Morning Courier & New York Enquirer,* seeing
"lightning . . . chained and subdued like a galley slave at
his oar," editorially urged investors to snap up the stock.

Famous men came to the shop at 42 Stanton Street to see
the new marvel, among them Samuel Morse, who was working
on his telegraph. A British patent was obtained, and there were
grandiose plans for selling the motors throughout Europe. But
months passed, and the partners did not receive the promised
payment. Cook demanded an accounting and suit was brought

against the promoter, who reported that he had used a large part of the stock proceeds for "expenses." Badly singed, Cook dissolved the partnership and went home.

Davenport resumed his bread-crust existence, living after a fashion by giving exhibitions of his toy electric railways. He plodded about calling on men of means, but depression had swept the country, New York mobs were storming food warehouses, and capital was hibernating. He planned to go to England to promote his motor, but couldn't raise steamship fare. This was his one piece of good luck. The ship went down.

By a stroke of publicity genius which might have redeemed him in better times, he launched a small magazine devoted to electricity, the first of its kind in the world. He drove the rotary press with his own one-half horsepower "electromagnetic engine." This was the first useful task ever performed by an electric motor. In its day it was a sensational triumph, but the zinc and acid used in his cumbersome wet batteries had to be renewed frequently, and the cost and trouble of this method would have been prohibitive if applied to more powerful motors.

Davenport wrote to his brother that since he couldn't afford a writer at ten dollars a week, he had filled the pages himself. The magazine failed. Still undaunted, he resumed publication under a new title. *The Magnet* appeared on July 4, 1840. Its *pièce de résistance* was the Declaration of Independence, which the inventor proclaimed he would "send by lightning throughout the entire world.

"We can scarcely conceive of anything more grand than bringing the electric spark to move the printing press," wrote the editor wistfully, and expressed high hopes for "liberal patronage." He could not buy paper for a second issue.

There was a false dawn before the final darkness. An Ohio man came forward with three thousand dollars, and Davenport, highly elated, saw vindication ahead. But the money was in Ohio bank notes, and he had used only ten dollars when he found that the bank had failed. That was the last straw. He collapsed with a nervous breakdown and found his way back to Brandon, where the loyal Emily was waiting for him.

He tried to shoe horses again, but found the work too strenuous. He and his wife settled on a small farm, where he stared at fallow fields he lacked the strength to till. He decided to write his memoirs, and dictated rambling, disjointed statements which Emily copied down. "I have found the power more controllable than the minds of men," he concluded, "and compliments more plenty than money." In a final burst of ingenuity, he invented an electrical attachment for a piano which would prolong its notes like those of an organ.

He was not quite forty-nine when he died. The patent on his motor had expired a few months earlier. Decades later, other men explored the full implications of the discoveries of Faraday and Henry and carried out Davenport's premature plans for a new epoch of power.

A. Ravielli

CHAPTER TWO

RUDOLF DIESEL

The Man Who Became an Engine

On the night of September 29, 1913, Dr. Rudolf Diesel, inventor of the motor which bears his name, was crossing the English Channel on the steamer *Dresden*. He was on his way to London to attend a meeting of diesel engine manufacturers and to confer with the British Admiralty concerning the use of his motor in naval vessels.

At about ten-thirty he said good night to two colleagues and went to his stateroom. The next morning when the boat docked at Harwich, he did not appear, and the steward was sent to rouse him. His berth was turned down, but had not been slept in. His nightshirt lay folded on the pillow. His watch had been carefully hung where it could be seen from the berth. But Dr. Diesel was not there, and he was never seen again.

His disappearance became an international mystery. There was a rumor that he had been abducted or killed by German agents to keep him from giving technical secrets to the British. There were hints of financial troubles and reports that he had run away and changed his name.

The mystery was never conclusively solved. In time it was forgotten, and today few people have heard of the mystery or the man. "Diesel" has become a word meaning an engine, usually written with a small "d"—perhaps the most lasting monument ever erected to an inventor.

Yet Rudolf Diesel was one of the greatest inventors of all time in the field of power and was honored in his lifetime throughout the world wherever engines ran. Unlike many inventors, he was no erratic amateur. He was a formally educated engineer who dedicated his life to the invention and development of a new "prime mover," an initial source of motive power. From the beginning he knew what he was about. He could hardly have planed a sticking door without first making a sketch of the work. That was the way he was brought up.

He was born of a line of German artisans, in Paris, in 1858. His father had emigrated from Bavaria and had finally succeeded in setting up a small leather-goods factory. Old Theodor Diesel was pious, well-meaning and stern. He saw in Rudolf the makings of a good mechanic. As soon as the boy could read, he made him sit still while he lectured to him on the functions of pulleys and levers. He took him to technical museums, and bade him study the first automobile,

Cugnot's three-wheeled steam carriage. Like most budding inventors, Rudolf dismembered the family clock. Unlike others, he could not reassemble it, so his father tied him to a chair as punishment. Ambition was running away with the boy, he said.

His mother brushed his hair German-fashion and sent him to school, a martyr among sleek Gallic lions. Like conditions have produced social misfits and criminals, but Rudolf turned to books and the company of his elders. He had a quick mind and was full of curiosity. He was always first in his class and he was a trifle smug about it. Once when he heard his mother telling a friend about someone who was very intelligent, he beamed. "You're talking about me, aren't you?"

When the Franco-Prussian War broke out in 1870, there was a spy scare in Paris, and all Germans were ordered to leave the city. The Diesels, included in the purge, fled to London with nothing but the clothes on their backs. They lost the factory and even their hastily-packed boxes of household goods. Rudolf, his parents, and his two sisters camped out in a two-room flat, using boxes for furniture. Theodor got a small clerical job, but the situation was precarious.

It was then that a cousin in Augsburg, a martinet professor of mathematics, offered to take care of Rudolf and send him to school. Rudolf made the trip from London alone. A letter went on ahead telling Professor Barnickel to watch at the station for a boy with a black woolly coat and a blue cap, and the stricter he was with him, the better.

Rudolf needed no disciplining. Books were his meat, and he won school prizes with ease. He dashed meteorically

through the Augsburg trade school, through the industrial
school, and then, to the dismay of his father, who thought he
should get a job, won a scholarship at the Munich Technical
Institute. When he had finished at the age of twenty, he had
broken every academic record in the institute, and the faculty
met him in a body and shook hands with him.

Two things more important than winning prizes happened
to Rudolf Diesel at Munich. He listened to a lecture, and he
saw a small gadget that looked like a popgun. The lecture was
given by Rudolf's favorite teacher, Dr. Carl Linde, who was
famous for his pioneer work in artificial refrigeration. He
spoke of the wastefulness of the steam engine. He pointed out
that when you burned fuel in a furnace, produced steam, and
conducted the steam through pipes to develop power in the
cylinder of an engine, energy was lost all along the line. The
best steam engines then in use, he explained, wasted ninety per
cent of the energy in the coal. Since then the efficiency of the
steam engine has been greatly improved, but while it has
other important merits, it still ranks low in the conversion of
heat into power.

Dr. Linde then told the class of the Carnot cycle, a method
existing only in theory, by which an engine could function
most economically.

Diesel listened with growing excitement, and scribbled
furiously in a notebook which has been preserved. He wrote:

"Mechanical theory teaches us that only a part of the heat
in the fuel can now be utilized . . . Doesn't it follow from
this that the utilization of steam, or any kind of go-between,
is false in principle? The possibility suggests itself of putting

the energy to work directly, without a mediator. But how can this actually be done? That is the problem."

The popgun-like gadget which Diesel saw at Munich was a cigar lighter used in the Far East. It is sometimes called a "Polynesian fire syringe." The air in the cylinder, heated by the compression of a plunger, ignites a bit of combustible material, providing a flame. This gave Diesel a hint as to how he could "put energy to work directly." (Of course he should have written "more directly," since he planned to eliminate the steam cycle and use only one "mediator," hot gas, to drive his engine.)

Behind Rudolf Diesel's great ambition there was something more than the desire to build a better engine and get rich. He was a humanitarian and something of a social philosopher, and he wanted to help small manufacturers like his father. He told his friends that since steam power could be produced more economically in large plants than in small ones, it favored big industry and tended to eliminate the family-owned factory. An engine more economical to operate over a wide range of sizes would tend to erase this industrial class distinction and aid in a more equitable distribution of wealth, he argued.

From that time on, the problem he had set for himself in his notebook was always with him, but fifteen years were to pass before he found an answer that suited him.

When Diesel left school, Professor Linde, who manufactured ice machines, made him his Paris agent at twenty dollars a month. Within a year he was a director of the company. He got married, and the children started coming.

After long days at the plant, he went home to work with slide rule and compass, formulating and scrapping plan after plan for the new efficient engine of his dream. Sometimes Mrs. Diesel found him in the morning asleep over his desk.

When he was thirty he said he felt like an old man and rebuked himself for having accomplished so little. He had turned out other inventions which were not profitable. He made a machine for freezing ice in cubes, but a cold winter brought a glut of natural ice, and it failed to catch on. An explosion of ammonia gas in the Paris refrigerating plant set him thinking, and he drew up plans for a new, humane military weapon—a bomb that would disable temporarily but would not kill. Military authorities were not interested.

Diesel was transferred to Linde's Berlin office, and the pages of diagrams and figures kept mounting on his desk. Finally he saw how his engine could be built. The popgun gadget had reminded him that the more you compress air, the hotter it becomes. If you put your hand on the rubber tube of a bicycle pump in action, you can confirm this fact. Now, reasoned Diesel, why not build an engine in which the piston pulls in nothing but pure air in its loading stroke and then drives back toward the cylinder head, compressing the air to about one-sixteenth of its former volume. Then, he computed, the air would be about one thousand degrees Fahrenheit, about the temperature of red-hot iron, and much hotter than the combustion point of oil.

At that point a drop of oil would be injected into the cylinder. The hot air would ignite the oil, and its combustion would drive the cylinder down. No spark ignition system would be needed, and his calculations showed his engine would apply a much higher percentage of the heat of the burning fuel to the business of making horsepower than any existing engine.

Simply phrased, this is the basis of today's diesel engine. One important reason why the diesel is more efficient than the gasoline engine lies in the difference in compression ratios. The diesel ratio is sixteen-to-one or better, while ten-to-one is very high for a gasoline engine. No matter how high the octane number of the fuel, no gasoline engine exists which would operate at the diesel ratio without disastrous knocking.

No layman's analogy can fully explain a scientific principle, but some are useful. We may say that the diesel piston, which travels fifteen-sixteenths of the way to the cylinder-head before combustion drives it downward, starts its working stroke from a higher jumping-off place than does the gasoline-engine piston. Two skiers have been used as an example— the one who starts near the top of the jump picks up more power than the one who starts farther down.

Placed in his shoes, a "monkey-wrench inventor" like Maxim, Lake or Edison would have built an engine at that point, but that was not Diesel's way. Everything about that engine, down to the last bolt, had to be figured out and put down on paper.

At length he took a manuscript to the printer, and the Diesel family went through an anxious waiting period. He had already taken out patents. In January, 1893, the work was published. *Theory and Construction of a Rational Heat Motor* was a slender pamphlet, but it belongs with that small shelf of books which have changed the world. A layman would

quickly get lost in its maze of curves, diagrams and mathematical formulas. Diesel knew that not more than a score
of men on earth would grasp its significance, and he was prepared for coldness and ridicule.

He got both. Scoffers called it a "paper engine," for it
existed only in a book. There was a whispering campaign that
he had appropriated ideas not his own, and certain men who
were afraid that the motor might injure their business spread
word that it couldn't possibly work. But there were a few technical men who accepted Diesel's conclusions, and their opinion
carried weight. Professors Schröter of Munich and Hartmann
of Charlottenburg backed him staunchly, and they had the
ear of the powerful industrialist Friedrich Alfred Krupp, who
agreed to finance the invention. Six months after the pamphlet
appeared, Diesel was building his engine in the Augsburg
Machine Factory.

In August, 1893, the motor was finished and ready for a
test. The inventor stood in the machine shop, anxiously watching an upright, pump-like contrivance with a slowly revolving
flywheel. The workmen looked on with friendly skepticism. No
engine like this had ever been seen before. The outlandish
thing took outside power to push the piston up and down.
Diesel waited impatiently. At last the moment had come. Eyes
blazing with excitement, face fevered from weeks of labor, he
pulled a lever and the vaporized fuel spurted into the red-hot
air.

There was a blast like a cannon shot, and chunks of metal
bombarded the room. Barely missed by death, Diesel leaped
to his feet with a shout of triumph.

"That's what I wanted to know," he said. "It proves I'm on the right track!"

Quickly he drew up plans for a second engine, in which the cylinder was water-cooled and the fuel was injected by means of compressed air. This engine developed power enough to turn over the flywheel, but it ran for only one minute. A third model came nearer the mark. But it was not until the fourth engine was turned out, almost four years after he had set to work in the Augsburg shop, that Diesel refuted his critics and proved that his theoretical engine kept all promises.

The world's most famous engineers flocked to Augsburg to see the twenty-horsepower "Dieselmotor." They made careful tests, and the results amazed them. The best steam engines of the day did not convert into power more than fifteen per cent of the heat value of the fuel used, but here was a new engine which at once showed an efficiency of more than thirty per cent.

Among the pilgrims who went to Augsburg was Colonel D. C. Meier, a New York engineer. Adolphus Busch, of the St. Louis brewing firm, was in Paris, on the point of sailing for home. When he heard that Meier was in Augsburg, he cancelled his passage and asked Meier to meet him in Paris. Meier told him that what he had heard about the new engine was true, and Busch jumped on the next train, wiring Diesel to meet him halfway. They met at Cologne and came to a rapid-fire agreement giving Busch the sole right to manufacture the new engine in the United States. Busch took his boat, and within a year a six-horsepower, two-cylinder diesel was set to work in St. Louis. This was the first diesel to turn a wheel in the United States.

The diesel engine made its first big inroads, however, in the more mature industrial climate of Europe, where the coal supply was already limited. It fulfilled some of the social goals for which Diesel designed it, but he could not foresee that it would become the chosen power plant for the German U-boats, any more than Einstein could know that one fruit of his formula, $E = MC^2$, would be Hiroshima.

In 1912, at the crest of his triumph, Diesel visited the United States. He was now Dr. Diesel. He lived in an impressive house in Munich, and money was flowing in from diesel plants in five countries. A New York engineer who showed Dr. and Mrs. Diesel around the city recalled a kindly, alert man in his early fifties, with thinning gray hair and slightly arched, inquiring eyebrows. American engineers were accustomed to arrogance from their German colleagues, but Diesel had come to learn. He asked innumerable questions about American resources in oil and coal, and the condition of the working man. He was feted at St. Louis, at Cornell, and at the Naval Academy at Annapolis. A speech he made before the American Society of Mechanical Engineers in New York left a lasting impression.

"Nowhere in the world," he said, "are the possibilities of this prime mover so great as in the United States." Yet it might be years before this development took place, he explained, for American industrialists were less interested in long-term efficiency than in big profits. With fuel cheap and plentiful, they wanted low-priced engines, regardless of operating cost, and the diesel, he said, was a comparatively expensive engine and always would be. Europe was far ahead of America in the use of the diesel, he added, because fuel costs were higher abroad, and industrial competition was keener. But he foresaw a time when America would be forced to turn to more economical operation. Then the great diesel boom would begin.

Dr. Diesel's prophecy has come true, for the United States leads the world in the production and use of the most efficient prime mover ever invented. Diesel's patents expired long ago, and now about two million diesel-type engines of all sizes and configurations are operating in this country. They range from giant installations of many thousands of horsepower used to run electric generators in factories, hospitals, big apartment houses and municipal power plants, down to tiny "dieseloid" motors which will drive model planes, and others that can be clamped on a bicycle to supplement pedal-power on hills.

As Diesel foresaw, his engines have in many cases served small industries as a "yardstick" competitor of electric utility companies in areas where electric power costs are high. On the rails they have virtually pushed the steam-driven "iron horse" into the last roundhouse. At first the diesel was a lumbering giant suited only for heavy tasks. Then smaller, lighter and more flexible engines were developed for automotive use. Today, about a quarter of a million diesel buses and trucks are running on American highways, and many more diesels are driving farm tractors, bulldozers and earth-movers.

Diesel passenger cars have long tempted manufacturers. In 1930, C. L. Cummins, an engine maker of Columbus, Indiana, bolted one of his diesels to the chassis of an old Packard and drove it to the Automobile Show in New York, making thirty-five miles to the gallon of kerosene-like fuel oil.

Since the engine is heavier and more expensive than the gasoline engine and vibrates more, its acceptance by American drivers seems unlikely. In Europe, where gasoline costs more than it does in the United States, the diesel passenger car has been widely adopted for taxicab use. Most cabs in London have diesel engines, and few riders notice the difference.

The fact that the diesel can use relatively cheap fuels instead of the highly refined gasoline needed by today's cars has contributed to its adoption for highway use. Yet in many parts of the world, taxation of motor fuels is eliminating this advantage. Oil economists point out that if it were possible for an automobile engine to burn water, a specially treated water would probably be sold which, after taxes, would cost the motorist as much as today's gasoline. The tax revenue would still be needed for highway maintenance. To the user, the diesel's really significant benefits are its superior longevity and the fact that it will do more work on a gallon of fuel. To society it has the great advantage of extending the life of our oil reserves.

Rudolf Diesel thought of this and looked far ahead to a time when the world's petroleum would be exhausted. He tested many odd fuels, among them powdered coal, but the problem of its scratching the cylinder has never been solved. He used, with some success, castor oil, palm oil, fish oil, and cotton-seed and peanut oils. Whale oil has been used as a stop-gap by Alaskan diesel-powered cannery boats, and a New York engineer once made a diesel run on rancid butter.

Tragedy was only a few months away when Dr. Diesel sailed for home after his American triumph, but those who saw the smiling, optimistic man to the boat said that his sudden death was the last thing on earth they expected. The following June, when a group of American engineers visited him in Munich, they found him genial and carefree. It is not surprising that when he vanished three months later, there were rumors of conspiracy and foul play.

Two friends were with Dr. Diesel on the *Dresden* that night. They were George Carels, a manufacturer, and Herr Luckmann, Carels' chief engineer. They dined well and then went to the deck for a stroll. Diesel was not only pleasant, he was jolly, Carels said later. At about ten-thirty they went below, and Diesel left the others when they passed his cabin. A moment later, he tapped on Carels' door, shook his hand heartily, and wished him good night. It seemed a little unnecessary. "I will see you in the morning," he said. Those were his last words. A member of the crew reported that he had seen Dr. Diesel alone on deck much later that night.

About a week later, a Dutch boat sighted a body in a high sea, and sailors managed to pull it aboard. It was battered beyond recognition, and after removing the contents of the pockets, they dropped it overboard. Later, Eugen Diesel identified as his father's a leather box for throat tablets, a coinpurse, a pocketknife and a glasses case with the name of a Munich maker. The finding of these articles convinced the family that Dr. Diesel was dead.

But with international tension at fever heat, and diesel-powered submarines straining at the leash, melodramatic stories quickly arose. It was rumored that he had never sailed on the *Dresden;* that he had left it at Harwich disguised as a

sailor and was hiding in Canada; that he had been pushed
overboard by German secret agents to prevent his selling plans
for a new engine to Great Britain. In 1917 a newspaper chain
printed an article, which it later repudiated, in which a man
who said he had served on a German submarine told how "the
traitor Diesel met the end he deserved."

Fresh light was thrown on the mystery years later in Eugen
Diesel's biography of his father. It seems that behind the
façade of his confident manner and his position of world
renown, Rudolf Diesel was at the end of his rope. All his
property was heavily mortgaged, and it was only a matter of
time before he would have to endure what was to him the
intolerable disgrace of bankruptcy. It was another case of a
brilliant intellectual who underestimated the shrewd abilities
of the business man. His income had been ample since Krupp
backed his engine, but he wanted a fortune to develop it
further and thought he could make it in Munich real estate.
At the start he did well. Then he plunged heavily and lost.
After that his affairs were hopeless.

In his desperation he turned to dubious schemes with
dubious men, and his son tells of a lottery plan in which his
partner cheated him. After his death it was found that he
owed $375,000, while his tangible assets came to only
$10,000. There were a dozen men who would have helped
him, but his stubborn pride would not let him admit his pre-
dicament, even to his wife. He spoke of selling the house, but
when Mrs. Diesel remarked that she was attached to it, he
airily discarded the plan.

He discussed methods of suicide with his son Rudolf, Jr.,

and the boy, never dreaming that his father was serious, said that he thought the best way was to jump off a fast-moving ship. When he left, his farewells were unaccountably affectionate.

Channel crossings are dismal affairs at best. He was alone after an evening of forced cheerfulness. Impending disaster must have struck him with double force. He went back on deck. Beneath him lay the dark, oblivious sea.

CHAPTER THREE

CHARLES GOODYEAR

"India Rubber Man"

In a South American jungle in 1736, Charles Marie de la Condamine, a young French explorer and amateur scientist, had trouble protecting his surveyor's quadrant from the tropical moisture. He noticed that the Indians made waterproof coverings from the coagulated sap of a huge tree common to the area. So he fashioned a case for his instrument from the same material, now known as "rubber."

Condamine was not the first adventurer to find this stuff. Many travelers, beginning with Columbus, had reported the existence of the curious elastic substance. Followers of Pizarro in Peru and Cortez in Mexico had described its use in some

49

detail. The Aztecs made balls from it for use in games, as
well as bottles, squirt guns, boots, toys and coated sheets.
Condamine, however, was the first fluent writer and talker to
tell Europe of the merits of *caoutchouc*, as it was then called.
He wrote about it in his widely-read books and discussed it
in the Paris salons where he was a welcome lion. He also
brought back samples of the redolent, spongy material. Soon
someone found that a hunk of it would erase a pencil mark,
and people began calling it "India rubber."

For decades, rubber was only an eraser and an amusing
curiosity. Nothing else bounced or stretched like it. A doll
made of rubber would grimace when squeezed. Now and then
rubber bottles and other articles, made by Brazilian Indians,
were brought to northern countries. Frederick the Great, who
popularized the potato, another South American discovery,
had a pair of riding boots coated with a solution of *caoutchouc*.
In 1820, the first pair of rubber shoes—gilded, with pointed
toes—came to the United States from Brazil. More followed
by the thousand, and they sold rapidly. In England, a chemist
named Charles Mackintosh made a syrup of crude rubber and
naphtha and used it to coat a fabric for the raincoat which still
bears his name. There was keen enthusiasm about the future
of the South American gum.

Then came the great "India Rubber Boom." Boston and
New York investors poured millions into fabricating companies, and large quantities of rubber shoes, caps, coats,
sheetings, life preservers, mail bags and other articles were
snapped up by eager purchasers at high prices. President
Andrew Jackson rode through the Boston rain in a rubber

suit while thousands cheered. Then the rubber bubble burst, factories closed, investors lost their money, and town dumps reeked of discarded raincoats.

The reason for the collapse was simple. In winter, rubber garments became as hard as boards. Daniel Webster left his raincoat standing alone before his house in Marshfield, Massachusetts, and passers-by confused it with the great statesman himself. And in summer heat, the rubber disintegrated into a sticky, gooey, foul-smelling mess. So in common parlance, an "India rubber scheme" became a synonym for a shady stock offering, and a slick or visionary promoter became known as an "India rubber man."

This was the state of the art of rubber fabrication in 1834, when Charles Goodyear of Naugatuck, Connecticut, was captured by the consuming ambition of his life. Alert scientists knew that rubber would be a wonderful material if it could be stablized. Chemists and tinkers of various countries were trying various recipes with no success. Where all others failed, Goodyear won out, but at a personal cost so appalling that his stubborn perseverance taxes belief. He was Disaster's favorite child. In his later life, he often read the Book of Job. No one was ever better trained to understand the tragic patriarch than the India Rubber Man, who, scorned, jailed, starved and swindled, never lost his faith.

Weighed by its impact on the life of man, Goodyear's vulcanization of rubber must be rated among the greatest inventions. It was destined to found a billion-dollar industry, launch the motor age, and reshape the world's technology. Goodyear might even be called rubber's creator, for rubber is simply a resilient material that will behave in a certain desirable and predictable fashion, and Goodyear was the man who made it behave that way.

Charles Goodyear was born in 1800 to a solid, prosperous Connecticut family whose forebears were prominent among the early settlers of New Haven. His father Amasa was a pioneer inventor and manufacturer of hardware, farm implements and "notions." At his factory at Naugatuck Amasa turned out spoons, scythes and clocks, and he made buttons for uniforms during the War of 1812. During his brief schooling, Charles thought of entering the ministry, but the call of his father's factory was stronger. He developed a passion for perfecting mechanical things. To him an inefficient door latch or spigot was not only a waste of good money, but "productive of great moral evil," as he soberly wrote. He also learned about the stubborn prejudices that often retard the adoption of new ideas. To supplant the clumsy, heavy, wrought-iron pitchforks which farmers were using, his father produced a light, strong fork of spring steel. For years farmers scorned the newfangled laborsavers, and the Goodyears had to give away dozens of them before they were widely accepted.

At seventeen the boy left school and was apprenticed to a Philadelphia firm of hardware importers until he should reach his majority. Hard labor impaired his health, and he developed a stomach condition which was to nag him for the rest of his life. When his term ended, he returned to his father, and the firm name became "A. Goodyear and Son." The new forks were now selling well and the Goodyears were financially secure. The great panic of the thirties was on the way, but no one knew it. Expansion was in the air. Charles, now married, returned to Philadelphia and opened the country's first domestic hardware shop, where he sold his Connecticut-made tools.

Always an optimistic and sincere talker, Goodyear became a star salesman. The firm built up a handsome bank balance, and the junior partner, still in his twenties, won high esteem among businessmen. Then for the first time he made his characteristic mistake of overextension with little margin of safety. He granted credit indiscriminately. Payments were slow, creditors clamored, and the company was forced to the wall. The Goodyears refused the relief of bankruptcy because they did not wish to lose title in a number of new inventions. They lost the factory, and they lost the fork monopoly which, by itself, would have kept the family in clover. And they were still liable for the firm's debts.

According to the profound legal logic of the day, if a man owed you money you could throw him in jail, thus depriving him of the opportunity of earning money to pay you. The Goodyears' notes had changed hands, and the new creditors were unsympathetic. The sheriff came and marched Charles to a Philadelphia prison, the first of many in which he was lodged at intervals throughout most of his life. He was patient and philosophical behind the bars, talked with his fellow prisoners, and remarked that it was a fine place to learn about human nature.

The debtors' law did not function fully in his case, for he managed to work while confined. His wife Clarissa brought materials and he turned out a mechanical improvement which

paid the household bills until he was released. For the next
ten years the creditors of the defunct hardware firm tossed
Goodyear in jail whenever the thought occurred to them, in-
variably at the most inconvenient of times. After that the
rubber creditors took over.

Goodyear—and the century—reached the age of thirty-
four before he gave a serious thought to rubber. It happened
almost by accident. Weary of business competition, he was
casting about for a novel idea or device, like his father's steel
fork, which might yield a comfortable living in an atmosphere
above the bickerings of trade. One summer day he was passing
the New York store of the Roxbury India Rubber Company,
and stopped to look at a life preserver. Although a land-
lubber, he always had a curious interest in life preservers,
which a psychologist might trace to a deep desire for security.
Annoyed at the awkwardness of the air valve in the inflatable
"doughnut," he went home and designed a better one.

The manager of the store gloomily agreed that Goodyear
had a better valve, but said that gadgets wouldn't help unless
someone found a way of making decent rubber. Articles decomposed by the heat were being returned daily, and the
firm was headed for the rocks. If Goodyear could find a
method of making satisfactory rubber, he would personally
guarantee him a fortune, the manager said.

Equipped with supreme confidence and complete ignorance
of the task before him, Goodyear secured a quantity of rubber solution and went home to experiment in his wife's kitchen.
From that time on, the all-enduring Mrs. Goodyear breathed

the odor of rubber messes and cleaned the clinging gum from her pots, pans and rolling pin. When she took bread from the oven, her husband was waiting to use the remaining heat to "cure" one of his concoctions. For several months Goodyear experimented eagerly. Sent to debtor's jail once more, he took his equipment with him and kept on mixing and testing his messes. He added a number of substances to the rubber mixture in attempts to remove its deficiencies, and had some success in making small samples of thin sheeting. His spirits soared, and he happily announced that he had solved the problem and was ready to begin manufacture.

Much impressed, a New Haven friend advanced a little working capital. Goodyear, his wife and two daughters and a few hired hands rolled the stuff thin on a marble slab and stuck it to a cloth backing. That winter they made hundreds of pairs of crude rubber shoes and stored them away to see what summer would do to them. There was no equipment for controlled temperature tests in those days, and every time Goodyear made an experiment he had to wait through the seasons to learn the results. The next summer the failure of this first venture was all too apparent as the neighbors held their noses. The shoes were fetid lumps, the winter's work was wasted, and the family was destitute. But Goodyear's courage was intact. Never for a moment during his long ordeal did he doubt that good rubber could be made or that he was the man to do it. He sold his household furniture to appease his creditors, found a country boarding house for his family, pledged Clarissa's chest of fine linen as security for their keep, and made a fresh start alone in New York. A friend supplied a small room, and a druggist let him have chemicals on credit.

Slowly and gropingly he was learning things about the mysterious juice of the Brazilian tree. Rubber was then shipped in turpentine, and he thought that turpentine might be the villain. So he secured some pure latex, and found that fabrics coated with it behaved equally badly. The rubber itself was at fault, he decided, and had to be reconstituted to become a worthwhile material. He mixed magnesia with the rubber and bound a book with it, but the covers soon became soft and sticky. Then he began to boil his batches in quicklime and water, "to tan it," he said. He obtained working space in a mill in what is now Greenwich Village. Every morning he prepared a jug of slaked lime in his room and carried it three miles on foot to the mill. He became a walking laboratory for his wares. Rain or shine, he wore a long rubber coat with areas variously stained for testing purposes, and he carried a hard rubber cane of which he was proud. Once a person looking for Goodyear was told:

"If you see a man with an India-rubber coat, India-rubber shoes, an India-rubber cap, and in his pocket an India-rubber purse with not a cent in it, that would be Charles Goodyear."

The lime-treated rubber was a complete failure. Even vinegar would dissolve it. Goodyear cheerfully crossed it off the books and tried another tack. This time he almost killed himself, but he made a definite approach toward his goal. Wishing to remove some bronze paint from a piece of rubber he had been decorating, he rubbed it with nitric acid. This discolored the specimen, and he threw it aside. Later he got curious about it, rescued the piece from the rubbish and found that it had a firm, smooth finish. Greatly excited, he denned up in his room and developed what he called the "acid gas process." While generating a large quantity of gas in his stuffy chamber he almost suffocated and was prostrate with fever for several weeks.

This was nothing to his fever of excitement over the piece of rubber sheeting he had produced. The stickiness was gone, and the samples appeared unchanged by the weather. Over-confident as usual, he proclaimed to the world that he had rescued the rubber industry, and when he was awarded medals for his discovery by the American and Mechanics' Institutes, the future seemed rosy. With promoter's zeal, he sent samples to President Jackson, Henry Clay and other notables, and printed a circular on rubber sheeting describing its merits.

A new angel appeared in the form of William Ballard of New York. Goodyear rescued his family from exile and rented a factory with steam power on Bank Street and a large building on Broadway for the display of rubber goods. He plunged into the manufacture of life preservers, shoes and raincoats. Then his backer failed in business, and the Good-years were again stripped to the clothes they stood in.

For several years the curve of the Goodyears' fortunes shot crazily up and down. After weeks of semi-starvation, Good-year would burst in loaded with groceries and presents, proclaiming that their troubles were over. There was a stay on Staten Island where the family lived in a shack and all hands worked in an abandoned rubber factory making articles which the inventor tried to peddle. They bartered and rationed their meager assets. A ring became a bag of flour and a watch chain was a pot roast. Then the curve shot upward. They moved to Roxbury, Massachusetts. Goodyear secured factory space, opened a store in Boston, and sold rubber table covers, capes and other articles treated with his "acid-gas." This process was only a makeshift and many defective articles were returned, but brisk sales kept the business in the black —until the next debacle.

The turning point of Goodyear's quest came in 1838 when he met Nathaniel Hayward, the last survivor of a closed Woburn rubber factory. Hayward had been experimenting with sulphur as a "drier" of India rubber. The idea came to him in a dream, he said. When he sprinkled it on his specimens and left them in the sun, the stickiness disappeared and the surface became smooth. He had also tried mixing sulphur in rubber compounds. Other manufacturers rejected Hayward's process because of the obnoxious odor of the sulphur-treated goods, but Goodyear bought Hayward's rights, hired him as an assistant, and spent on experiments money which he was to need for food before the year was over.

Meanwhile, Goodyear's press-agentry had borne fruit. The government gave him a larger order for mailbags. Seeing, as usual, the bright dawn of fortune, Goodyear finished the bags and hung them up. He was absent from the plant during a hot spell. When he returned, the bags had dropped from their handles and were rotting like dead fish. The acid-gas method, Goodyear discovered belatedly, gave only a superficial finish and was useless with rubber goods of any thickness. This point was further emphasized when several thousand decomposed life preservers, which had been sold throughout the country, came back from their enraged buyers. Goodyear's commercial reputation was gone, and no man of business would help him. Friends of the family told him that he was getting what he richly deserved and implored him to be sensible and return to hardware. Once again the Goodyears went through the wringer, and all their household goods were sold at auction.

"The inventor now applied himself alone, with unabated ardor and diligence, to detect the cause of his misfortune." Charles Goodyear wrote that sentence in his memoirs—which he printed on rubber—in telling of his attempts to find out why the mailbags melted. There was no going back for him. He was a "rubber man" for life, and bore all the scorn the phrase connoted. He resumed his experiments, managing to gather a few cents now and then to buy needed materials.

One night in January, 1839, he finally made his great discovery. It happened at a house in Woburn where he was stopping. According to one report, he had promised Clarissa that he would abandon the quest and look for a paying job, and was there without her knowledge. Working over a wood stove, he was testing the effect of moderate heat on the mailbag rubber, which contained some sulphur. Holding a strip in his hand, he was gesturing while he talked with his brother Nelson and two other rubber men who were present. The rubber came in contact with the hot stove, and he suddenly became silent and stared at it. His rubber had always melted when it got too hot; this piece was charred like leather where

it fell against the stove. He had discovered at last the true
secret of vulcanization—that rubber, treated with sulphur
and subjected to a high degree of heat, became firm, stable
and durable. Goodyear didn't know what had happened—
he only knew that it worked.

"Vulcanization" is only a word derived from the name of
the Roman god of fire, and does nothing to explain Goodyear's discovery. Knowledge of how the process really works
is still incomplete, but modern chemists tell us that crude
rubber is composed of long molecular chains of carbon atoms
which are not hooked together laterally. In that form, the
material is plastic. It can be shaped or molded in any form
desired, but will not retain the desired form without further
chemical treatment. Sulphur hooks these chains together, acting somewhat like the cross-links in a tire chain, although
the structure is much more complex. The softness, flexibility
and stretchability of the rubber can be controlled by the
number of cross-links built in during vulcanization—the
greater the number, the stiffer and harder is the rubber. After
vulcanization, the rubber is no longer sticky, but dry and
firm, its strength is greatly increased, it wears much better,
and it behaves the same at all normal temperatures.

Many stories have been printed about Goodyear's "accidental discovery," with the implication that anyone might
have made it. Goodyear justly resented this oversimplifica-
tion. In his own account of the discovery, written in the third
person, he stated:

"It may be added, that he was many years seeking to accomplish this object, and that he allowed nothing to escape

his notice that related to the subject. Like the falling of an apple, it was suggestive of an important fact to one whose mind was previously prepared to draw an inference from any occurrence which might favor the object of his research. While the inventor admits that these discoveries were not the result of *scientific* chemical investigations, he is not willing to admit that they were the result of what is commonly termed accident; he claims them to be the result of the closest application and observation." Whoever reads of other "accidental" discoveries" will do well to recall Goodyear's words.

One hundred years later, a statue of Charles Goodyear was unveiled in Akron, Ohio, America's "rubber capital," to memorialize the discovery he made that night, but the men who witnessed the experiment paid little attention to it. The neighbors heard that the India rubber man had had another brainstorm. For the next year he performed repeated experiments, using different temperatures, different "cooking" periods, different thicknesses of rubber, different amounts of sulphur, and introducing many other variables. He found that kitchen stoves were not hot enough, and made a nuisance of himself in Woburn and Lynn factories, where foremen often allowed him to cure his specimens in their furnaces. He begged shamelessly, both for food for his family and for materials for his work, for he believed that he was an instrument of Providence and that if he died before completing his mission, his great discovery would not survive him.

Moved by his intense sincerity, neighbors supplied driblets of aid and comfort. Without a cent to his name, he decided to build a brick oven for curing his rubber. A friend let him use a site in a factory yard, and he traded a batch of rubber work aprons for the bricks and labor. The first batches of rubber goods were spoiled, and Goodyear's helper, Hayward, threw up his hands and walked out. Month after month, the oven belched acrid smoke while Goodyear and his brother Nelson improved the technique of vulcanization. Important recognition came eight months after Goodyear's discovery from Professor Benjamin Silliman of Yale. He was one of the country's most influential scientists, and many struggling inventors, including Thomas Davenport, were grateful for his timely praise. Silliman tested samples of Goodyear's rubber and gave him a written statement endorsing his claims.

Meanwhile, things were getting no better at the Goodyear house in Woburn. That summer, the children dug potatoes half-grown; they had nothing else to eat. Book by book, Goodyear sold his library, and after grim soul-searching, raised five dollars on the children's schoolbooks. A crisis came the following winter, during a long and biting snowstorm. Shivering in the unheated cottage were Goodyear's parents, four small children and his pregnant wife. So ill that he could hardly walk, Goodyear plodded several miles through the rising drifts to the home of a prosperous citizen, Oliver B. Coolidge. There he showed his rubber samples and made his familiar plea. Coolidge came to the rescue and supported the family for the rest of the winter, gravely accepting mortgages on Goodyear's rubber stocks and chemicals.

Soon businessmen were listening to Goodyear seriously. But there were still cruel and humiliating blows, almost too painful to relate. Once more in debtor's prison, he wrote to potential backers, asking them to confer with him "at his lodgings." In Boston to raise funds, he was locked from his hotel room because he couldn't pay his bill, and walked the ten miles back to Woburn. When his two-year-old son died, the body was taken to the grave in a farm wagon. By his two marriages Goodyear had eleven children, and five of them died before they reached the age of four.

After his son's death, kindly people who believed not in rubber but in humanity, came to the family's rescue with cash and supplies. Other men found money for his work. William de Forest, his boyhood tutor, who had become a prosperous manufacturer and later married the inventor's sister, advanced the first of several sizable sums. In New York Goodyear found another backer who financed his manufacturing project until the backer lost his money. It was not that a loan to Charles Goodyear was the kiss of death, but rather that any man who would back a rubber goods factory during those tentative days of experimentation was the sort of man who would probably lose his money anyway. Goodyear had the answer, but it took time and money to develop it.

He opened a plant in Springfield, Massachusetts, devised new machinery to exploit his great discovery, and was on the threshold of success when his old hardware creditors threw him in jail again. He said that it was "as good a resting place as any this side of the grave." He finally went through bankruptcy, but later paid the creditors, although his debts had been discharged.

Soon the Goodyear curve began to rise. The vulcanized rubber goods sold briskly, and this time few articles were

returned. In 1844 he received a patent for the process, and
manufacturers purchased licenses to make all manner of
articles. At that point he could have accumulated a large fortune, had he not been Charles Goodyear. But the future of
rubber meant more to him than wealth, and he spent money
lavishly on experiments. He thought everything should be
made of rubber. He spent months making a rubber sail, which
was tested with some success in Atlantic crossings. He printed
sample newspapers on rubber, and even suggested rubber
smoking pipes, pianos, violins, coal hods and banknotes.

His naïve generosity in passing out samples of his rubber
and describing his processes lost him a fortune. Two years
after his discovery, he gave some samples to a young English-
man, who took them home. Later they fell into the hands of
Thomas Hancock, who for many years had been trying without success to stabilize crude rubber. He smelled the sulphur,
succeeded in duplicating Goodyear's work, and obtained a
British patent a few days before Goodyear received his American patent certificate. Goodyear's patent was also widely
pirated by American manufacturers while he was busily
dreaming of rubber as the "universal material" of the future.

Spurred by his licensees, he finally took action against
Horace H. Day of New Jersey, who claimed to have discovered
vulcanization himself and was using Goodyear's process without payment. The result was "The Great India Rubber Case,"
one of the leading industrial suits of the century.

Because Goodyear's name was stamped on so many products, the public regarded the inventor as a heartless Croesus

and wept for poor Mr. Day. Day hired Rufus Choate to plead his case. There was only one lawyer in the country who could top Rufus Choate—the seventy-one-year-old Daniel Webster, then Secretary of State. It was incredible for a man in his position to take the case, and he was harshly criticized for doing it. But he was deeply in debt and convinced himself that it was his duty to his creditors. Lured by a fee of ten thousand dollars and five thousand more if he won, the god-like Daniel entered the lists against the devil of infringement. Choate and his colleagues produced a number of obscure experimenters who claimed credit for Goodyear's work. This was Webster's meat. Rising for his final kill, the weary warrior demolished their "shreds and patches of testimony," and delivered a eulogy of Goodyear and his "elastic metal" which brought cheers from the crowd. And after his tribute to the patient Clarissa, all eyes were wet. The court issued a perpetual injunction against Day.

The decision could not protect Goodyear against his enthusiastic improvidence. Money not spent on experiments went for ballyhoo. At England's Crystal Palace Exhibition in 1851 he showed a suite of rooms in which everything was made of rubber, and he produced an even more lavish show at the Paris exhibition four years later. Louis Napoleon called for him and took him for a drive, and he was awarded the Cross of the Legion of Honor. But Goodyear luck persisted. He could not pay the contractors who had set up his exhibit, was prostrated, and was hauled off from his sickbed to Clichy jail, where the decoration was brought to him. Later he was arrested in London and became so ill that he barely recovered.

Clarissa died during the stay in England. There was a year of loneliness. Then a courageous young Englishwoman married him and shouldered the family burdens. In 1858 he brought his family to America, after pawning his wife's jewelry for the passage. Then his fortunes improved, and he bought a house in Washington, where he enjoyed a brief year of peace.

In the summer of 1860, a broken man, he attempted a journey to New Haven to visit a dying daughter. He reached New York and could go no farther. Surrounded by his family, friends and physician, he met death, at least, in comfort and dignity.

Charles Goodyear labored twenty-six years to make rubber the servant of man, and died some two hundred thousand dollars in debt. His work founded many fortunes, yet the meagerness of his reward never seems to have disturbed him. "Man has just cause for regret," he wrote, "when he sows and no one reaps."

He left behind him hundreds of suggestions for uses of the material he fashioned, many of which are now commonplace. He preached rubber bands for securing packages, and rubber for hot water bottles, surgical gloves, sheets, syringes, "squeegees," rattles, balls, inflatable pillows, pontoon rafts and lifeboats. He thought of a vacuum-sealed sack to preserve foods, now being made from synthetics, and the future may resurrect many another Goodyear suggestion. About the only rubber article he never thought of was an inflatable tire.

Goodyear's rubber came from tree sap. Today, huge chemical plants are also making rubber from petroleum, alcohol and a dozen other things. The new rubber, like the old, is virtually useless until vulcanized by Goodyear's process, so a mighty, new industry has ·been built upon the invention to which he devoted his tireless, tragic life.

CHAPTER FOUR

ALFRED NOBEL

Dynamite and Prizes

One day in 1861 a group of Paris financiers gave impatient audience to a young Swedish inventor. He was a thin, sickly, nervous man, with penetrating blue eyes and plenty of assurance. He announced dramatically that he had an oil which would shake the globe.

Alfred Nobel calmly went on to explain his new explosive. After a while, they cut him off, ridiculing his claims. But when the Emperor Napoleon III heard about the violent oil, he didn't laugh. He used his influence, and Nobel went back to Stockholm with a draft for a hundred thousand francs. Within a year, he and his father were manufacturing nitroglycerin for commercial use. In a few years the world was startled by a new word—dynamite. And the foundation was laid for the Nobel fortune the income from which is now distributed annually to scientists, writers, and workers for peace, for distinguished achievement in their fields.

To Alfred Nobel, there was nothing sinister about powerful explosives. He and his father and brothers had been working with them for years. Old Emmanuel, an architect turned inventor, could make anything from a field gun to a jack-in-the-box. From the time he was six, when he fashioned a piece of ice into a burning glass and lit his father's pipe with it, he was full of ideas. Some of them were brilliant. His hot-water central heating plant was installed in Stockholm hospitals. He thought of using rubber for carriage tires and of using porous rubber cushions for carriage seats. Other plans were more spectacular. He proposed catching young seals and training them to answer to their names and obey orders. In wartime he would tie bombs to their tails and send them to blow up enemy ships.

Emmanuel's income varied as much as his ideas. Despite the patient efforts of Mrs. Nobel, the family was often in trouble. They moved frequently and not by choice. When the landlord wanted cash, Emmanuel showed him blueprints. His enthusiasm was contagious, and sometimes the landlord forgot that the sketches were not legal tender. The year Alfred was born, 1833, was one of the times when his father couldn't pay the rent. The creditors were not beguiled, and Emmanuel was thrown into bankruptcy.

Four years later, when Emmanuel was working in his laboratory with bottles of strange concoctions, there was a sharp explosion which broke the neighbors' windows. There was an indignation meeting, and the Nobels were ordered to leave Stockholm. That was only the beginning. Creditors took their bills and went to court, and Emmanuel was threatened with prison.

In the nick of time a Russian emissary arrived at the Nobels' door. He had heard that Nobel had invented a naval mine, and he wanted him to come to St. Petersburg and put on a demonstration for Czar Nicholas I. Emmanuel packed his papers and reported to the Russian war department. The Czar's generals followed him at safe distances while he set off blasts in fields and quarries, and admirals watched him explode his black-powder bombs beneath the sea. War was brewing, and the government gave him money to start a factory in St. Petersburg, with the condition that all his inventions would be placed at Russia's disposal. The Crimean War broke out. The British fleet sailed to attack Kronstadt, encountered Nobel's mines, and turned back. Nobel began to make marine engines for the government and also obtained a long-term contract for infantry rifles. He started work on a factory which would employ a thousand men and branched out with a dozen new ideas for the improvement of explosives. The Czar decorated him and gave him a gold watch. Emmanuel Nobel was the man of the hour.

Alfred was only four years old when his father left for his Russian triumph. He was the third of four brothers and was the puniest of the lot. As a baby he had convulsions, and for years his mother fought a constant battle to keep him alive.

He had a weak spine, and when other children were playing he sat on the sidelines and envied them. He had nervous headaches and a poor digestion and was extremely sensitive to criticism. At the age of eight he was sent to a private school in Stockholm, where the teachers considered him brilliant. After a year his father sent for the family, and formal schooling was ended. In St. Petersburg Emmanuel hired tutors for the boys, who appear to have received a thorough grounding in philosophy, languages and literature.

Ludwig, the second son, was his father's favorite. Ludwig had genius, said Emmanuel, but Alfred worked harder. This remark seems to have irritated Alfred, and although he was constantly going to doctors and taking medicine, he never missed a chance to show his daring. Once when the brothers were going to work at the Nobel plant on the other side of the Neva, and the ferry wasn't there as usual, Alfred jumped into the river and swam over. His brothers scolded him, and the men at the factory made fun of him. He walked out in a white rage. He didn't come home that night, and his brothers scoured the city for him. Days later, he strolled into the house casually. He said he had been making a trip into the interior and refused to say more.

At the age of sixteen, Alfred left home for an indefinite period of travel, education and adventure which has never been fully explained. It began when Emmanuel heard glowing reports of a heat engine built by his fellow-countryman John Ericsson, who had migrated to New York, and who was soon to revolutionize the world's navies with his ironclad *Monitor,* of Civil War fame. Emmanuel wanted one of his sons to study the engine at close hand and couldn't spare Ludwig. So he sent Alfred, with instructions to work in Ericsson's shop, learn about the engine and complete his technical education. Alfred sailed for New York, but no one knows how long he stayed in the United States or what he did. If he took the job with Ericsson, he did not remain long, and we can make what we like out of the fact that the boy was impatient and irritable and that the lonely Ericsson, then in his fifties, was crusty and eccentric. Alfred soon returned to Europe and seems to have made only a perfunctory report on the engine his father was interested in.

Alfred rambled aimlessly here and there, explored Paris night life, turned from it in disgust, and met a young girl with whom he fell desperately in love. She died, and he walked the streets all night, saw the sun rise, and wrote a long, introspective poem which he was to treasure all his life and read to people who seemed sympathetic.

The prodigal eventually returned to his father's factory. Bitter, disillusioned and hardened, but cherishing secret ideals which seemed impossible to realize, he went resolutely to work, for work, he decided, was all that life held for him. Emmanuel Nobel had then become interested in the possibilities of nitroglycerin as an explosive. The compound had first been made in 1846 by Ascanio Sobrero, professor of chemistry at the University of Turin in Italy. He had discovered its explosive properties, but had decided that it was too dangerous. It was commonly called "glonoin oil," and before Emmanuel began work with it, it was used mainly as a drug in the treatment of angina pectoris. (It is interesting

to recall that petroleum was also used as a drug before it became a fuel.)

Emmanuel and Alfred were less concerned about safety
than was Sobrero. They mixed the oil with gunpowder, filled
bombs with it, tossed the bombs into lakes and rivers, and
watched columns of water spurt up. This was risky business,
for the reaction could not be plotted with any certainty.
Alfred carefully checked the results, and came to a decision.
He would tame nitroglycerin and make it work.

This program was rudely interrupted, for once again disaster struck at old Emmanuel. For about eighteen years he
had led his idea of the perfect life, which meant that he had
plenty of money to make things with and people left him
alone. Now his great patron, Czar Nicholas, died, and the
new government of Alexander II canceled Nobel's contract
for infantry rifles. On the strength of that contract, Emmanuel
had spent all he had for new equipment. Now everything
seemed lost, and his plant went into receivership. Emmanuel
growled savagely at Alexander's perfidy. Years later there
was a sort of poetic retribution when Alexander was as-
sassinated by a bomb filled with the dynamite invented by
Alfred Nobel.

Emmanuel and Mrs. Nobel and Emil, the youngest son,
went back to Stockholm, as poor as they ever had been. Alfred,
worn out by overexertion, collapsed, and Ludwig stayed behind to look after him and to pick up the pieces of the business. Ludwig, every bit as smart as his father thought him,
eventually built a huge industry from those pieces. He secured more rifle contracts, went to the Caucasus to find walnut

wood for butts, found oil there, set up refineries and pipe lines and made millions. In the nineties, if you spoke of Nobel, people said, "Do you mean the dynamite king or the oil king?" But in 1859, when Emmanuel glumly went back home, the future "kings" were closer to being paupers.

As soon as Alfred recovered, he joined his parents and brother in Stockholm. They lived a hand-to-mouth existence, Emmanuel pawned the Czar's watch, and for a time they seem to have run a milk shop.

This state of affairs hampered Alfred in his plan to control and direct the terrific force of the strange oil, which was then little more than a scientific curiosity. But this time, he had taken the lead, and Emmanuel followed after. Sometime during Alfred's unexplained years he had picked up a good working knowledge of chemistry, draftsmanship, and mechanical engineering.

Commonly called "soup," nitroglycerin looked more like salad oil. Its behavior was unpredictable. Sometimes a container of the stuff would fall to the ground with a thud, and nothing would happen; at the other times a small jolt would cause a shattering explosion that would knock a strong building into rubbish and break windowpanes half a mile away. Even when stored away and treated with great respect, it might develop explosive fumes. It was devilish, treacherous stuff.

Little by little, Alfred Nobel got around to the theory that the only sure way of exploding this liquid was to confine it in a stout container and set it off with a sharp primary explosion. First he tried putting a glass tube of the soup into a metal container of gunpowder and setting off the powder with a fuse. Then he reversed their positions and put a small cylinder of gunpowder inside a sealed can of the soup. Finally he evolved the blasting cap, a small copper cylinder filled with mercury fulminate and open at one end to permit the insertion of a fuse. In a nutshell: a match wouldn't explode nitroglycerin; it took force. So Nobel used an intermediary which would provide the force and could be set off with a match.

That invention is the basis of the whole nitroglycerin and dynamite industry. Nobel had found a way to explode the soup at will and with great effect. Today everyone who builds a dam, a canal, a subway or a mountain road uses one of the descendants of "Nobel's Patent Detonator."

Even after Nobel had secured backing with the help of Napoleon, and he and his father had set up their first plant, Alfred's brothers were skeptical and tried to discourage him. "Give up inventing," Robert wrote from St. Petersburg. "You should turn your attention to more serious matters." That was in May, 1864. Four months later, Robert's admonition was given more weight by a ghastly tragedy.

Neither Emmanuel nor Alfred was in the shop that morning. The youngest son Emil, who was only twenty-one, was in charge. A mechanic and two other employees were there, and a passing workman had dropped in to see what was going on. There was an explosion, and everyone in the room was instantly killed. Old Emmanuel was prostrated. He had a paralytic stroke from which he never recovered. He lingered for years, and from his bed or wheel chair continued to turn out ideas and inventions which Mrs. Nobel faithfully recorded.

It seems likely that he had read Poe's grisly essay "Premature Burial," which swept Europe in his day, for he designed a coffin "so constructed that a person coming to life could lift the lid from the inside, the lid being provided with airholes for breathing, and with a cord attached to a bell."

Stockholm shook with terror at the news of the explosion, and wild rumors went around about the eccentric Nobels and the new monster which they had unleashed. The Nobels had no permit to work with explosives, and the authorities took action. But meanwhile, engineers and miners everywhere heard of the new timesaving, money-saving blasting oil. When Hannibal crossed the Alps, the only way he could make a path for his elephants was to heat the obstructing rocks with fire, pour vinegar on them, and wait for them to crack. Gunpowder simplified such jobs, and now the Nobel concoction pointed the way to another great advance. Orders and inquiries came in from all over the world.

Alfred Nobel moved his plant to a barge moored in a lake and went ahead with production, making flying trips to the Continent to interest capital. Within a year he had launched manufacturing companies in Sweden, Finland, Norway and Germany, and the Swedish government was using his "soup" to blast a terminal railway tunnel under Stockholm. Chemist, manufacturer, bookkeeper and salesman all in one, he hardly took time to eat and succeeded in ruining his digestion for life. Men with money to invest wanted demonstrations. Handling nitroglycerin often gives people headaches, and it affected Nobel violently, but he would allow no one else to run the risk. Sometimes when setting a blast in a mine shaft he would collapse and lie on the ground for several minutes. But he refused to spare himself. He would show them, he said, that his blasting oil was safe. He was too optimistic; nitroglycerin's reign of terror was about to begin.

One Sunday morning in November, 1865, a dozen thirsty New Yorkers were lined up at the street-level bar of the Wyoming Hotel on Greenwich Street, near the North River.

"Mike," said one of the men, "what smells so funny?" The bartender sniffed and told the hotel's boy-of-all-work to take a look around. It was surely a funny smell. Some of the customers helped the boy investigate. One of them opened a closet door and ran back holding his nose.

"It's that box," said the boy. "The box I've been using to shine shoes on. A man named Lührs got off the boat and left it here."

Two of the men lifted the box. Reddish smoke was coming out of it. They shoved it through the swinging doors to the street. There was a blast like a dozen Fourth of Julys rolled into one, and the men dropped to the floor under a mound of broken bottles. Fortunately, no one was killed. Mayor Hoffman ordered an investigation. It was nitroglycerin. On the same day a Westphalian miner went to a store and asked for two pounds of blasting oil. The clerk started to pour it out, and that was the last of the clerk, the miner and the store. At about the same time, Nobel's nitroglycerin plant in Norway soared skyward. A few weeks later, a railroad worker in Silesia thought he could cut frozen blasting oil with an axe. They found his legs half a mile away.

The next April, the steamship *European*, pride of the West

India and Pacific Company, docked beside the Long Wharf at Aspinwall, Panama, now called Colón. On the other side of the heavy-timbered wharf was her sister ship the *Caribbean,* and at the shore end stood the massive three-hundred-foot freight house, built of stone with iron girders. At seven the next morning a deafening roar shook sea and land, and a giant force played jackstraws with beams, winches, girders, and lifeboats. The *European,* the wharf, and the freight house were reduced to ruins, and the *Caribbean* was badly disabled. Sixty people were killed, and the damage came to a million dollars. Seventy cases of nitroglycerin, marked for San Francisco, had blown up in the *European's* hold. Company officials reported that they were labeled "glonoin oil," and that in accepting the shipment they had been unaware of its nature.

A few days later a freight wagon, bearing several oil-stained wooden boxes, drew up before the office of the Wells Fargo Company in San Francisco. The driver said, "Whoa!" and that was his farewell to life. Fifteen persons were killed, many were injured, and a two-hundred-thousand-dollar block of buildings was wrecked. The shipment of nitroglycerin was traced to Nobel's New York agents.

Other nitroglycerin catastrophes followed, many of them due to ignorance and carelessness. A German teamster used the oil for wagon grease, with fatal results; another man used it for oiling harness; a sailor filled the cabin lantern with it; a porter threw a box of it off the top of a stagecoach. One man was lucky. An Indian carrying a box of "soup" skidded on a wet gangplank at Fargo, North Dakota, did aerial acrobatics while the boat crew stood frozen with horror, landed right side up in five feet of water holding the box over his head, and shrieked, "Me no go happy hunting ground!"

Alfred Nobel arrived in New York on a business trip a few days after the San Francisco blast, bearing some boxes of nitroglycerin. He was about as welcome as the plague. The newspapers had aroused the public, and Fire Marshall Baker was investigating rumors that parcels of "the murderous compound" were stored in lofts and warehouses. People avoided Nobel, and hotels turned him away. His associate, Colonel Otto Burstenbinder, had been taken into court, and Nobel was called as a witness. Nobel wrote a letter to the papers, asserting that his explosive was less dangerous than gunpowder and offering to prove it in a public demonstration. The *New York Herald* ran a derisive editorial predicting Nobel's "departure skyward."

On the morning of May 4, Nobel took his bag of tricks and went to Nolte's quarry at the corner of 83rd Street and Eighth Avenue, a spot which was then in the country. About twenty men came to see the demonstration, keeping their distance. First, Nobel brought out a flat piece of iron and laid it on a rock. He poured a little of the terrible oil on the iron and then raised a hammer. The spectators ducked for cover as the hammer descended. There was a sharp report, but Nobel was unharmed. He coaxed them nearer and in a dry, scientific manner explained that only the oil struck by the hammer exploded. There was the rest of the puddle, undisturbed. "You couldn't blow off the lot," he said, "without confining it." Then he touched a match to the puddle. It burned, but it didn't explode. For two hours Nobel made the mysterious giant jump through hoops. The New Yorkers drew around him in a circle and finally handled the packages. Nobel finished the performance with some real blasts, to show what the giant would do when you gave him his head. The crowd went away convinced.

But governments were not convinced, and neither were transportation companies. Several countries passed laws forbidding the use of nitroglycerin, and because of the Panama disaster, ships refused to carry it. Although Nobel's office was swamped with orders and a fortune was within his reach, he almost failed that year.

Nobel had learned belatedly that his job was only half finished. He had taught the beast to bite, but he hadn't provided a muzzle. A safe way of packaging the explosive had to be invented. The Panama Canal, Boulder Dam, the Union Pacific Railway, the New York subways and all the world's heavy industries were waiting for it.

Nobel tried many methods. When he mixed the oil with wood alcohol, he found that it was safer to ship, but it had to be separated before use, and that was too delicate a job for most miners. Finally he found the solution. In northern Germany there is a light, absorbent earth called *kieselguhr*. Nobel's workers ran out of sawdust and used it in packing nitroglycerin cans. One of the cans leaked, it has been reported, and Nobel noticed that the *kieselguhr* soaked up the oil like blotting paper. Nobel mixed three parts of "soup" with one part of *kieselguhr*, and his prayers were answered. The stuff could be kneaded like putty and packed in cartridges, it could be exploded with a blasting cap, and it was safe to ship. Nobel borrowed the Greek word for "power," and "dynamite" entered the language. Production leaped ahead. Within a decade, fifteen Nobel plants were turning out the new explosive, and annual sales ran to more than six million pounds. Later, Nobel was to invent a more concentrated explosive known as "blasting gelatin," a smokeless powder for military use, and many other things, but his fame as an inventor rests upon dynamite, and dynamite made him rich.

Alfred Nobel is now considered the founder of the explosives industry. His *kieselguhr*, which was an inert substance and did not contribute to the explosion, was supplanted long ago by a combination of active ingredients—nitrates and carbonaceous materials like corn meal, starch and wood flour —which greatly increased the explosive strength. The modern product, however, was made possible by the principles discovered by Nobel.

Many uninformed people have seen a sardonic inconsistency in the fact that dynamite's inventor founded a peace prize and have falsely assumed that his disposal of his fortune was an act of contrition. Actually, dynamite is one of our greatest *industrial* tools. It cannot be used in a rifle or cannon, since it explodes so rapidly that it would burst a gun. Its manufacture is so different from that of smokeless powder that a dynamite plant cannot be turned into a munitions plant in time of war. Dynamite's use by political radicals has always inspired cartoonists, but its more constructive uses have received less public attention. For example, twenty-one million pounds of dynamite were used in digging the ninety-two

miles of tunnels in the Colorado River aqueduct, which supplies water to Los Angeles. The job was done in six years.
Without dynamite it is estimated that at least a thousand
years would have been needed to complete the work. One can
find similar examples all over the world.

Nobel was a complex and difficult man, who never was,
and never pretended to be, endowed with the sunnier virtues.
He perfected other explosives for the munitions trade, which
he pursued realistically. For his great invention, dynamite,
civilization is greatly in debt to him.

There were really two Alfred Nobels—the tough-minded
inventor of explosives and the somber, despairing idealist. At
the age of forty he found himself a lonely, exhausted, melancholy man, with no interests outside his work and few ac-
quaintances outside his companies. He had money enough to
satisfy any taste, but he could not relax, and he didn't know
how to go about enjoying himself. He didn't even have a
home. They called him "the richest vagabond in Europe."

He tried to make himself over. He bought a fine house in
Paris, furnished it richly, and filled the conservatory with
exotic plants. He bought blooded horses and a fine carriage
and took lonely drives in the park. He bought some paintings
which some people found rather "pagan." He got bored with
them, and made an arrangement with an art dealer to take
them back now and then and give him other ones. There
were few things he could eat because of his stomach trouble,
but he installed a good chef, began to entertain, and took
great pride in his wine cellar and his table appointments. He
returned to reading Shelley, the god of his boyhood, and had

an idea of writing something worthwhile. He was equally at
home in Swedish, Russian, French, German, English and
Italian and never could make up his mind which language he
should use. Even in conversation he wandered from one
tongue to another, unconsciously slipping into the language
which the topic suggested. Late in life he wrote a play and
was completely wrapped up in it. He went to London for a
business conference, talked business for five minutes, then
brought out his play and read it. The play was about to be
published when he died. His executors looked it over and
thought it best to burn the edition, saving only three copies
for the files.

Madame Juliette Adam, noted hostess of the day, asked
him to her salon, but he had nothing in common with her other
guests and suspected that he was being exhibited as a horrible
example. Women got a shuddery thrill out of meeting "the
dynamite king." After a few experiments of this sort, he
snorted and withdrew into himself. He thought of making his
own house into a meeting place for intellectual leaders, but
his friends pointed out that this was difficult without a hostess.
He considered marriage, but since his early love affair he
hadn't met a woman he thought he could get along with. He
made cynical remarks about women, but those who drew him
out found that he was desperately shy and that he believed
himself to be so repulsive that no woman would marry him
except for his money. Yet whenever an attractive woman
made a determined attempt to be nice to him, his crust melted
like snow beneath the springtime sun. If ever a man was in

a mood to appreciate a charming, mature woman, it was Alfred Nobel.

In Nobel's study there was a secretary's desk, but it was usually vacant. His correspondence was in six languages, and it was not easy to find a good secretary and an accomplished linguist in one person. He hated to hire secretaries, because he dreaded dismissing them.

In 1876 he tried once more, inserting this notice in Continental newspapers: "A very wealthy, cultured, elderly gentleman, living in Paris, desires to find a lady also of mature years, familiar with languages, as secretary and manager of his household."

Nobel's advertisement soon played a part in a painfully polite interview in a Vienna mansion between a certain Baroness von Suttner and her children's governess, thirty-three-year-old Countess Bertha Kinsky, a talented, penniless member of the Viennese aristocracy. There was a crisis in the house. The handsome twenty-six-year-old son of the household, Baron Artur von Suttner, had come home in disgrace because he had failed in his law exams, and Bertha had offered to coach him. They had fallen in love. The night before, there had been a dance. Bertha and Artur had met alone later, and the Baroness had surprised them. The match seemed entirely unsuitable; there was the difference in age, and Artur was expected to promote the family fortunes by selecting a bride with a dowry.

There was little to say. Bertha proferred her resignation, and the Baroness thoughtfully showed her the interesting

notice in the morning paper. Bertha answered the ad and
received a reply from the "dynamite king." An interview in
Paris was arranged. Looking for an "elderly gentleman" at the
railway station, Bertha was approached by a dark-bearded
man of forty-three, with a shy, kindly manner. And the "lady
of mature years" turned out to be a handsome, statuesque
woman, young for thirty-three, with finely chiseled features
and huge, appealing dark eyes.

Nobel drove Bertha to her hotel and took her to luncheon.
He found her a good listener and talked at length about
politics, art, life, time, eternity, and the future of mankind.
Then he showed her his house and the suite where she was
to live as his household manager. She was never to occupy the
rooms. After a few days, Nobel left for Stockholm on a business trip. Then Bertha received a telegram from Artur von
Suttner, which read, "I cannot live without you." She wrote
Nobel a letter of thanks and apology, pawned a piece of
jewelry, and took the next train to Vienna. She and the young
Baron were secretly married and left for Mingrelia in the
Caucasus, where Bertha had family friends. For a time they
lived precariously. Then both became successful journalists
and essayists. The big turning point in their lives came when
Russia declared war on Turkey, and the Caucasus became
an armed camp.

After watching the young men march off, seeing them return
on hospital trains, and observing at close hand the privations
and despair caused by war, Bertha became an ardent pacifist.
During these years, Bertha and Alfred Nobel had continued
by letter their Paris conversations. She and the Baron visited

him in Paris, where he dined them, showed them through his laboratory, and talked of his experiments. There ensued a long debate about means to end war. Nobel praised her idealism, but was amused by her vehemence and for a time treated her as an attractive nitwit unaware of the facts of life. He told her he knew a better way of ending war. "I would like to produce a substance or machine," he said, "of such frightful efficiency for wholesale devastation that wars should thereby become altogether impossible. Let the Sword of Damocles hang over every head, and you will witness a miracle. War will instantly stop." Yet he developed a deep interest in her peace movement.

With a keen sense of the value of his support, the Baroness pursued her advantage and asked him to attend a peace congress at Bern, Switzerland. He refused, but when the von Suttners arrived, they found him installed in a hotel. He didn't want to meet people, he insisted, but asked for a specific report of the proceedings. He invited the von Suttners to visit him at Zurich for further discussion. They spent long afternoons on the lake in his aluminum motorboat. He sneered at the "gas bags" in the peace movement and scoffed at banquets and speeches. People who expected immediate disarmament, he told the Baroness, were simply making themselves ridiculous without doing any good. Attack the problem piecemeal, he suggested—let all nations agree to a "cooling-off" period of one year, perhaps. If he were satisfied with the program, would he help out, she asked him.

"Yes, I would," he replied. "Inform me, convince me— and then I will do something great for the movement."

The Baroness then decided that the peace movement needed a book about war that would shock people, so she plunged into research about the more repellent aspects of battlefield carnage. The result was a fat novel, *Lay Down Your Arms,* in which she poured out all her pain and rage. Today, neither the realism nor the ideas in her book would cause a ripple, and readers would yawn at the long philosophical dialogues, but it filled a need in 1889 and was a great popular success. Called everything from a "shattering document" to "preposterous hackwork," it swept the world in twelve languages and was pirated in Russia. The Baroness von Suttner's name was on every tongue, and she automatically became a world leader in the peace movement. She held seats of honor at dinners and congresses, drafted resolutions, toured the United States where she was received by President Roosevelt, and founded a monthly magazine named for her novel. Leo Tolstoy compared her book with *Uncle Tom's Cabin.* But her most valued tribute came from Nobel. He praised the "charm of her style and the grandeur of her ideas," and predicted that these "weapons" would carry much farther than the newest guns "and all the other implements of hell."

Nobel finally decided that he would leave his fortune, which came to about nine million dollars when he died, to found a prize for distinguished workers for peace. Later he included the prizes for science and literature. It would be foolish to assume that the hard-bitten tycoon thus disposed of his fortune solely because of the Baroness' importunities. He weighed the plan for years and discussed it with many able people and left only a part of his gift to her cause. But she saw in him early a gruff idealism which sought expression, and waged her campaign with great charm and perseverance. Her part in the matter was widely recognized. When the first Nobel Peace Prize was awarded in 1901, Henri Dunant, co-winner, wrote to Bertha von Suttner and thanked her. The prize was her work, he said. It seems fitting that four years later the peace prize went to the Baroness herself.

Alfred Nobel ended his days in austere solitude in his luxurious villa at San Remo, Italy. He had turned his back on Paris when the French government, alarmed because he had sold his smokeless powder to Italy, had placed restrictions upon his work. When his brother Ludwig died, the French papers thought it was Alfred. Nobel had the peculiar satisfaction of reading his own obituaries. They were not complimentary.

At San Remo he spent most of the time in his laboratory, working on synthetic rubber and artificial silk. His heart began to give out, and he laughed when the doctors prescribed nitroglycerin. He bought a sphygmograph, watched the line which showed the irregularities of his pulse, and pointed out to friends the degree of variation that would kill him.

When his family asked him for a short autobiographical sketch, he made humorous suggestions, among them, "He took care of his own nails and was never a burden to anyone." On December 10, 1896, he died. At his request, his body was cremated, for like old Emmanuel, he was afraid of being buried alive.

Before his death Alfred Nobel abandoned the idea, common at the time, that more powerful killing agents would frighten the nations into keeping the peace. "High explosives will not deter men from waging war," he said to a friend. "The number of victims in future wars will be greater, and the tax payers will have an even larger burden."

At first, Nobel did not intend to found a perpetual peace prize. He suggested that it be discontinued at the end of thirty years, for he believed that if international peace were not assured by that time, the world would infallibly relapse into barbarism. He said that in 1893.

A. Ravielli

CHAPTER FIVE

SIMON LAKE

And His Submarines

In the summer of 1882 at Toms River, New Jersey, a pudgy, red-haired, freckled boy of fifteen built a clumsy canvas canoe from directions he found in a magazine. Then he took another look at his craft and saw it as something else—a testing device to determine a man's oxygen requirements. Simon Lake had read *Twenty Thousand Leagues Under the Sea* at the age of ten, and he had decided with complete assurance that someday he would build a better submarine than Jules Verne's fictional *Nautilus*. For one thing, he thought Verne's diving compartment was too dangerous, and he needed some basic data about air supply. So he tipped the canoe over and

93

stuck his head underneath to see how long he could breathe. His first experiment was ruined by a neighbor who thought he was drowning. His only timepiece was a watch he had made from spare parts which would not run except on its back. In spite of handicaps, he finally estimated that he could trap enough air to last him for about half an hour, and set about planning more precise experiments. He had already drawn up tentative plans for his first undersea boat, and in 1894, the *Argonaut, Jr.*, made successful trial runs.

Twenty-one years later, a descendant of Lake's tiny craft —his plans had been turned down by the U. S. Navy and pirated by the Germans—torpedoed the *Lusitania* and sent her to the bottom with a loss of 1,198 lives, 124 of them American. This tragedy, dramatizing the Kaiser's decision to launch unlimited submarine warfare, enraged the American people and spurred the vacillating President Woodrow Wilson. It was an important, if not the determining factor in destroying the delicate balance of American neutrality and bringing the United States into World War I in aid of the Allies two years later.

History offers few more pat examples of the social and political results of an invention, and speculation as to the course of events if the boy had not read Jules Verne's book, or had stuck to his father's foundry, is a tempting guessing game.

Simon Lake, creator of a brutal instrument of death, was a quiet, kindly, sober, religious man, brought up on the Bible and the strict code of fairness to all men which was the proud heritage of his early-American artisan family. He was, of course, aware of the wartime potentialities of his invention and drew a sketch in 1893 showing a submarine firing a torpedo at a battleship, but war was something of a gentleman's game when Simon was a boy. Throughout his life, he was eloquent about the humane uses of his craft. He saw submarines harvesting oysters, reclaiming sea-bed oil and minerals and salvaging sunken cargoes. He believed they would become economical freight carriers and would cruise in the Arctic under the ice. He made many other inventions now forgotten, but to the day of his death, at the age of seventy-eight, he poured his sturdy life force into the perfection and promotion of the boat that swam beneath the sea.

Simon Lake came from a family of mechanics and inventors who never bought a machine if they could build it. "In our house," he recalled later, "drawing boards and calipers were household necessities." Grandfather Lake had invented a seed-planting machine, and Simon's father had invented a window-shade roller which was commercially successful. Other Lakes invented an early typewriter, an offset device for color printing, a pre-Bell telephone which worked, and a successful shoe-lasting machine.

Simon's Uncle Jesse Lake, who had a couple of schooners and a foundry, had much to do with encouraging the boy's bold imagination. He greatly impressed Simon when he told him, with all the authority of his hard-packed two hundred and fifty pounds, that if he had a cable long enough and something to tie it to, he could pull the earth and the moon together. Once he took a contract to build a road over a marsh, but the ground was so soft that his horses were mired. With his unconventional inventor's eye he looked at his horse treadmill, a stationary power machine then commonly used. It had an endless belt, paved with wooden cleats and set at an incline on a stout wooden frame. Horses walked on the incline, turning the belt. The belt turned a drivewheel over which it passed, which in turn ran circular saws and other machines. Jesse turned the machine upside down and transformed it into something very similar to a modern caterpillar tractor. Now when the horses climbed the incline, the cleated surface crossed the mire, distributing the horses' weight and enabling them to pull the wagon. Later he built a tractor driven by a steam engine, which was used to build the first highway over the swampy ground from Pleasantville, New Jersey, to Atlantic City.

Not all Lake inventions were successful. Jesse built some buoyant wooden shoes for walking on water, but when he tried them out on a creek, he capsized and was held, head down in the water, until help came. Then he and Uncle Ezra, a minister, invented a flying machine. Ezra made the first test flight in a gallery of his church and tried to fly to the opposite gallery. He landed in the pews, and the project was abandoned.

So when Simon approached his father with plans for a submarine, he received grave consideration. To build a submarine, said his father, he would need more schooling. But formal schooling did not agree with Simon. No one could tell him about submarines, so he committed outrageous pranks and finally left school. He enrolled as an apprentice mechanic and took part-time courses at the Franklin Institute in Philadelphia.

When Lake chose his life work around 1880, the submarine was already an ancient device. During several centuries, scores of underwater craft of sorts had been built and tested. None of them worked very well, and they drowned or asphyxiated hundreds of crewmen. The great Leonardo da Vinci drew up plans for an "underwater warship." There are reports that a Greek named Scyllias descended in a kind of diving bell to cut the anchor cables of Persian ships and that Alexander the Great was lowered in a barrel with glass ports so that he could observe marine life.

The first naval engagement between a submarine and an enemy ship took place on September 6, 1776. An odd, one-man craft, the *Turtle*, invented by David Bushnell, a scholarly Yale student, slipped beneath the surface of New York Harbor to attack the flagship of Admiral Howe, the British naval commander who was blockading the city. The *Turtle* was a pear-shaped oak barrel with a hand-cranked propeller, a rudder, and a porthole through which the operator could spot his prey. It carried a time-bomb to be attached to the hull of a wooden ship by means of a screw. The attack failed because the British hull was copper-clad. The pilot set off his bomb in the harbor to annoy the enemy and returned safely to base.

Robert Fulton's *Nautilus* attracted wide attention in the early 1800's. Napoleon Bonaparte helped finance the craft with a view to destroying the British Navy. She was first tested in Brest harbor, where she blew up an old schooner as a demonstration for French admirals. She was an ingenious boat, with a cylindrical hull, a hand-cranked propeller, and an umbrella-like collapsible mast and sail for surface propulsion. She had ballast tanks that were flooded to make her submerge and compressed air tanks for expelling the water to make her rise to the surface. All modern submarines have a similar system. Napoleon turned Fulton down, as did Great Britain and the United States. Discouraged with submarines, he set to work on a steamboat.

After Fulton's failure, submarine invention lagged until the Civil War, when the Confederates built a number of weird craft in attempts to break the Union blockade. One was the *Hunley*, an undersea boat made from an old boiler and named for Captain Horace L. Hunley, who financed her construction. She was a jerry-built deathtrap, apparently designed by a committee. Eight sweating, gasping heroes lay in her stinking belly, turning a long camshaft, which ran the propeller. Many of them never came out. She killed more than thirty men, including Captain Hunley, and was sent on her last mission only as an act of desperation by the trade-strangled Confederacy. On February 16, 1864, zealous young Lieutenant George E. Dixon from Alabama persuaded his superiors to let him try to sink the Union gunboat *Housatonic*, one of the ships which bottled up Charleston Harbor. He drove his time-bomb into the gunboat and sank her, but the bomb went off prematurely. The *Hunley* and her crew also went to the bottom, but she became the first submarine to sink an enemy ship in battle.

While the young Lake was planning his first submarine, his great American rival, John Philip Holland, a frail, aging Irish schoolteacher who wanted to sink the British Navy, was working on undersea boats with equal ardor. When Lake was only eleven, Holland had built the *Fenian Ram* for Irish "home rule" patriots. It behaved erratically, and later he built another submarine, which was also a failure. Nursing his wounds, Holland was temporarily in retirement.

Such was the state of the submarine art when Lake launched his underwater career. He was convinced that all previous submarines were wrong in principle. Most of them, including Holland's, had to dive like porpoises to go down. This often piled the crew up in the prow of the boat; it made control difficult, and sometimes the boat stuck her nose in the bottom and remained there. Lake planned an "even-keel submersible," a submarine which by means of projecting vanes fore and aft would retain its horizontal position while submerging. His experiments proved his basic principle to be correct, and it is now used in every submarine the world over.

That was only one of the problems which Lake met and solved in the long years of experimentation before he actually built his first submersible boat. Science in those days could throw little light on the things Lake needed to know. There was the matter of air supply. Lake could find no solid answers and had to find out for himself. He took a paper flour bag, rolled it up to expel the air, put the opening to his mouth, and exhaled until it was full. Then he breathed the air in the bag and found that it made him sick. He built a large airtight wooden box and cooped himself up, watch in hand, to find out how long he could stand it. From these tests he estimated the volume of air he needed per hour.

Not all of Lake's conclusions were correct. At Johns Hopkins Hospital in Baltimore he learned that "bad air" was exhausted from the contagious wards through outlets in the floor. This must mean that bad air is heavier than good air, he decided, and shut himself up in his box to test his theory. He lit matches, raised and lowered them, and as the minutes ticked by, found some evidence that his exhaled carbon dioxide, a gas in which fire will not burn, tended to settle near the floor. As a result, his plans provided for the exhaustion of bad air through the floor of his submarine compartments. Later on, when one of his crew panicked and thought he was suffocating, Lake dispelled his fear by lighting a candle and placing it on the floor. Since there was still oxygen enough at that level to support a flame, there was no cause for alarm, he explained.

Much research has been done since then, and it is now known that while exhaled gases, which are a little heavier than oxygen, do tend to settle in closed spaces, they settle only gradually, like the solids in a bottle of liquid shoe polish left on the shelf a long time. Any motion of a submarine or of crewmen nullifies this tendency of gases to stratify by weight. So while his ventilating system worked, his theory was wrong. Many excellent scientists and engineers have arrived at similar false conclusions which have later been refuted. Lake's experiments were important because they show how hard he was willing to work in an attempt to discover the truth.

In Jules Verne's fictional *Nautilus* there was a compartment through which divers could emerge to investigate the ocean bed. Lake decided that he needed an underwater exit in his submarine. It was a matter of opening a door on the sea and at the same time keeping the water out—obviously impossible, people said. Lake was thinking it over one evening when his eyes fell on an old powder horn left by a pioneer ancestor. The horn had a small measuring compartment near the tip. When this space was full of powder, an inner valve closed, and the outer one could be opened to pour the charge of powder into the musket barrel. Such measuring devices are now used on beverage bottles. Lake saw the answer to his problem, and hastily blocked out plans for his submarine "air lock." It was a small, airtight room with two doors, one opening into the interior of the boat, the other, a trap door, opening to the sea. He could enter the room, release compressed air until the pressure was high enough to keep the water out, then open the sea door. You can understand the idea by turning an empty milk bottle upside down and forcing it down into a full bathtub. Crews could collect oysters and crabs through the open door or don diving suits to salvage wrecks. To Lake, this means of sea-bed exit was one of the most important features of a submarine.

For twelve years Simon Lake put in his evenings and odd moments planning his ship. Meanwhile he earned an ample living working in the family foundry and from inventions that were more immediately remunerative. His safety device for windlasses on oyster boats, which prevented the wheel from spinning backward and striking the operator, sold well. He used to row out in the bay and attach the devices for thirty-five dollars each, and did not know till years later why they were so popular. They reduced the noise of the windlasses, enabling "oyster pirates" to work private beds undetected. He also invented a device for bicycles which allowed play in the steering wheels, the principle of which is now used in all automobiles. This device was patented when he was twenty. During the next fifty years, more than two hundred patents were granted to him in the United States and abroad. One hundred and eleven of them had to do with submarines; more than ninety helped to improve all manner of everyday mechanical devices.

He grew up and married. His wife, while caring for three children, entered with enthusiasm the atmosphere of gear-wheels and blueprints. One day in 1892 when he came home from work, she met him at the door with a newspaper. The Navy, aroused at last to the value of underwater boats, was advertising for bids. At last the *Argonaut*, the name which Lake had given to his "paper" submersible, would become a solid reality. So Lake confidently believed.

In high spirits he took the train to Washington on the appointed day with his plans. He knew his boat, he knew his competition, and he had no doubt whatever about the outcome. But he had never done business in Washington before and was unprepared for official indifference and delays. He spent two days in an anteroom, and then was curtly dismissed after a brief interview. Again and again he tried to reach the ear of someone who would listen, but he was a simple mechanic, none too well-dressed, without money, influential friends or political acumen. Years later he was told that four out of five members of the Naval Board of Construction had approved his *Argonaut*, but for a number of complicated reasons the contract of one hundred and fifty thousand dollars went to his rival, Holland.

Holland proceeded to build the eighty-five-foot, cigar-shaped *Plunger,* which was a clumsy failure and was never commissioned. The blame was not entirely Holland's—the Navy insisted on changes he did not approve of. Holland later built many successful submarines and deserves high credit for many of his ideas. Throughout his life, Lake always spoke of his rival with respect, but insisted that his basic approach was unsound.

Bruised by his battle with bureaucracy, Lake declared that he would never go to Washington again until they called him. Years later, after Russia, Germany, Austria and England had adopted his submarine, the call came.

But Lake could not wait for staid admirals who had spent decades winning their stripes and, quite naturally, resented brash civilians who might send them back to school. Determined to build his ships and prove his case, he went to Wall Street in search of a backer. But Russell Sage, a prominent financier, had just been attacked by a crank, and when the shock-headed stranger talked about a boat that would roll on the bottom of the sea like a tricycle, he found inner sanctums hard to enter. No longer able to pay for his room, he took the train home. He decided to scale down his plans and build a small model from cheap materials. No one seemed to understand his ideas but the other Lakes, and the family came to his rescue. An uncle and aunt, Mr. and Mrs. S. T. Champion, offered to advance a few hundred dollars for material, and his cousin Bart Champion said he would help build the boat.

Later, while turning out powerful sea monsters for the world's navies, Lake always recalled the building of the fourteen-foot *Argonaut, Jr.,* as the greatest adventure of his life. She was a stubby, boxlike craft covered with two criss-crossed layers of pitch pine, with canvas between. She had tanks which could be flooded with water to offset her buoyancy so that she would submerge. On her bottom there were three wooden wheels, sawed from a log like those of a primitive oxcart. The front one was for steering, and two rear ones were driven by a crank inside which was turned by manpower. Lake's cherished idea, the air lock, with its trap door into the sea, was built into her stern. They found an old soda fountain tank for compressed air to hold back the water when the sea door was open, and a secondhand plumber's pump to fill it with. Air for breathing came through a pipe from a buoy on the surface, and as a final touch, there was a small gasoline stove for cooking fish speared through the trap door.

The launching of the *Argonaut, Jr.*, took place with no fanfare. Lake and his cousin Bart trundled the crude ark to the Shrewsbury River and risked their lives on Simon's calculations. Everything worked according to plan. They screwed down the hatch, flooded the tanks and sank to the bottom, then cranked the machine across the river bed and back. That summer, Lake and his cousin had the time of their lives. A new world of strange, underwater creatures and plants had been opened to them. As fish peered through the portholes in the eerie silence, Lake reaped the first great reward of his years of labor and planning, fortified his belief in the future of underwater craft, and made notes for the giant submarines he was to build in the years ahead. They poked around the bed of New York Bay for clams and oysters, and Lake went out through the sea door in his homemade diving suit, with sash-weights tied to his legs, to explore the bottom.

With renewed confidence, Lake planned to build the *Argonaut I,* the full-scale craft which the Navy had turned down, and sought "big money" to form a company. His uncle approached Nathan Straus, and the New York financier came to the pier with his wife on a blazing hot day to see the ship go through her paces. Things went well until an excursion steamer went by and her bow wave knocked the little sub against the dock and damaged her mechanism. Repairs would take hours. The Strauses left, and Lake's opportunity was gone.

So Lake decided to attract "little money," and gave a public demonstration attended by the leading people in Atlantic Highlands. When Lake brought up objects from the bottom they suspected a trick, so he proposed a test. The doubters wrote their names on a shingle, tied a weight to it, and threw it in the water. Lake and his cousin Bart submerged the craft and went down and retrieved it. That was one of many tests which resulted in the sale of stock to form the Lake Torpedo Boat Company and the construction of America's first successful full-scale submarine. The thirty-six-foot, all metal, gasoline-powered boat went through its trial runs with flying colors, rode out the roughest of storms, and attracted attention all over the world.

Lake transferred operations to Bridgeport, Connecticut, and gave a big party on board for the mayor, other notables, and the press. He took his twenty-eight guests to the bottom of

the harbor, where they took turns entering the diving compartment and raking clams for souvenirs. They cooked a fish dinner, and John J. Fisher, a popular singer of the day, entertained with "Rocked in the Cradle of the Deep" and "Down
Went McGinty." It was such a good party they were two hours
late in coming up, and they found the dock jammed with a
horror-stricken populace who had given them up for dead. A
wrecking boat had been sent for, newsmen were writing obituaries, and an editor denounced them for holding up his presses
for nothing.

Curiously enough, Lake and his rival Holland worked in
adjoining rooms at a Baltimore plant while Holland was building his ill-fated *Plunger* under government contract and Lake
was building his privately-financed *Argonaut.* They passed
each other every day, confining their comments to the weather.
Despite the proved merits of the *Argonaut,* it had little chance
with the Navy after the *Plunger* fiasco. To most people, a submarine was a submarine.

Aware of his debt to his stockholders, many of them friends
and neighbors, Lake looked into every opportunity to fill the
coffers. The Cuban rebellion against Spanish rule had broken
out, and a committee of exiles approached him with an offer
of three million dollars for the *Argonaut.* There were two
conditions: the sum was to be paid after the revolution succeeded, and the boat must first be approved by a patriot admiral. As usual, Lake was jubilant at the faintest sniff of
success and proudly took the admiral for a trial run. But
when they entered the air lock and the pressure began to rise,
the admiral developed claustrophobia and released a salvo

of Spanish curses. Negotiations were canceled. Many times in his career, Lake missed a fortune by a hair.

After war broke out between Spain and the United States in 1898, Lake took the craft to Hampton Roads, explored the channel floor on her iron wheels, and recorded the location of some experimental mines set out by the Navy. Then he told Naval authorities what he had done and showed them how easily an enemy sub could put mines out of action and cut cables. They did not believe him until they found his data correct. Then they denounced his action as espionage and threatened serious trouble if he did such a thing again.

Meanwhile, Holland had secured the backing of the powerful Electric Storage Battery Company of Philadelphia, which saw a new market for its batteries in undersea boats. Free of bureaucratic interference, the long-suffering schoolteacher built a much improved craft, the *Holland*, which was accepted and commissioned by the Navy in 1900. Soon the Navy ordered six more Holland boats. Lake was left far behind, but still had his loyal following.

Lake plugged away at improvements in his Bridgeport laboratory and drew up plans for a bigger and better submarine. He saw what others were discovering, that the submarine needed better eyes above the surface when submerged. He went to optical firms and asked them to make some sort of tube with lenses which would serve the purpose. They declared flatly that it was impossible. That word had lost its meaning for Lake, so he bought a miscellaneous assortment of some two hundred lenses from a retired optical man, found a German craftsman who could make right-angle prisms, and began to experiment. He built a tubelike box and stuck the end out of his office window, then adjusted the lenses in various positions in an attempt to get a view of the street. His chance of success was slight, but after several months and hundreds of experiments, he finally looked in the tube and saw a clear view of the street. Then he went to lunch, it started raining, and the office boy pulled in the tube and jumbled up the lenses. Despairing of ever setting them aright, Lake went to a Johns Hopkins scientist for help. The expert had never heard of such a device, but he took Lake's data and in about a week succeeded in repeating his experiment. So Lake had a periscope for his next submarine. Later he learned that Sir Howard Grubb of England had devised a similar instrument.

Soon high officers in the Navy showed renewed interest in a Lake submarine. There was no appropriation, but they promised to do their best to secure adoption. Lake raised more money from his stockholders to build the sixty-five-foot *Protector*, designed for coastal defense. He called on William Howard Taft, then Secretary of War, and Taft promptly sent three Army officers to see the boat in action. The *Protector* passed grueling tests. She submerged for ten hours, she navigated under the ice, and she simulated the laying of mines. The investigating board made an enthusiastic report, and the Senate voted to buy her, but then the bill was killed in conference. Lake later learned that the deciding voice was that of a Midwestern glove manufacturer.

Things were getting tight at the Lake plant. Once he had to shut down because he couldn't meet a bill for seventeen dollars.

Then in 1904 Russia and Japan went to war, and both sides sent agents to make bids for the *Protector*. A patriotic man, Lake did not wish to sell the weapon to a foreign power, but it was the only alternative to bankruptcy. He weighed the merits of the belligerents and chose Russia. Then he found that the shipment of war materials to either power would raise problems. Secrecy was essential. The outlines of a submarine were not easily recognized then, so he had her hoisted to the deck of a freighter, covered with tarpaulin and shipped to Russia. Lake followed, taking the name of "Elwood Simon," to help the Russians conceal their plans.

The Russians had devised a stiff test. The fleet harbor at Libau was virtually an inland lake, protected by breakwaters and reached by a winding channel that taxed the abilities of even surface pilots. To pass the test, a submarine had to start from the open sea and thread this maze to the harbor beneath searchlights without being seen or heard. Two diving-type subs and Lake's *Protector* were tried out. Both "divers" were disqualified, for they bobbed to the surface when they encountered obstructions. Lake's "even-keel submersible" felt its way along the winding trail left by the dredges and popped up beside the battle fleet in good torpedoing position. Later, Lake went to Kronstadt and introduced himself to Admiral Rodjestvensky by rising from the water beside his flagship.

"I don't like your submarine!" snapped the admiral. "Russia needs more of them."

The Russians shipped the *Protector* across Siberia on special railway cars, and she was stationed in Vladivostock Harbor. More orders followed, and eleven Lake submarines were eventually built for Russia. Had Lake gone to Russia two years earlier, Japan's fleet instead of Russia's might have gone to the bottom, with interesting political consequences.

Lake's wife and children joined him in Russia, and they spent about two years there. He was offered an attractive contract to remain, but the Lakes found official Russian life too sophisticated for their tastes and decided to bring up their children in Connecticut.

Despite Russia's failure to utilize the submarine fully, Lake's stay abroad shaped history in a manner he could not foresee. Krupp, the German arms firm, examined Lake's plans and offered him a contract. Then they discovered that Lake's patents were not protected in Germany and tore up the contract. Admiral von Tirpitz became a convert to offensive submarine warfare, and Lake's patents were appropriated to build Germany's U-boat fleet.

Lake's fame as a submarine builder was now international. Eventually the walls of Jericho toppled over, and he sold a ship to the U. S. Navy. The 161-foot *Seal*, commissioned in 1912, quickly made world records, and Lake received contracts for five more boats. With the First World War, he came into his own. In his shipyards at Bridgeport and Long Beach, California, he built more than forty submarines for the Navy.

In the period between the two World Wars, Lake revived his early ambitions for peaceful uses of the submarine. He became interested in the plans of Sir Hubert Wilkins for exploring the Arctic beneath the ice. He had advocated under-ice navigation in 1899, and now he gladly contributed his time toward rebuilding an old Naval submarine for the purpose. The expedition sailed before Lake considered the boat ready, and mechanical trouble developed. But the voyage proved the practicability of traveling under thick ice. Lake's dream has since been handsomely realized by the Polar voyages of nuclear submarines.

In 1932, Lake spent a large sum of his own money building a submarine called the *Explorer*, designed for deep-sea scientific research, prospecting for off-shore oil deposits, salvaging cargo in sunken barges, oyster-gathering and treasure-hunting. Her trial runs were successful, but the venture was a financial failure and drained away most of his capital. Several times in his life he had amassed enough money to retire in comfort. Twice he tried to retire, once by travel and once on a Connecticut farm, but fresh plans drew him back to his drawing board.

When World War II broke out, Lake was overlooked while younger men, using his discoveries, built the nation's submarines. His white-pillared colonial house in Milford, Connecticut, which he had bought in prosperous days, had been sold under mortgage foreclosure, and he was dependent on whatever he could earn. He calmly moved to more modest quarters and continued work. To him, money was a tool to be used in the development of new ideas, and he seldom thought about it until it was gone.

In 1942 Simon Lake was living alone in a Pottstown, Pennsylvania, rooming house and working with a local firm on a method which he had developed for the rapid drying of concrete by means of vacuum and heat, making possible thinner and less expensive structures. Such methods have been used since with dramatic success.

Then a great-grandfather of seventy-five, deliberate in pace and diction, his courage was still intact. One eye was almost closed, for the muscles had been injured once when he had collided with a periscope in a rough sea. The other eye gleamed from his ruddy face with a steady flame as he discussed his plans. He liked to pore over a map of the seacoast of western Europe, in which shorelines were surrounded by black dots, each dot showing where a ship once went down.

"Looks like caviar, doesn't it?" he used to say. "Someone once estimated that all the world's shipping goes to the bottom every twenty-five years. On the bed of the sea lies the wealth of Croesus. Some day, submarines will reclaim it."

He died in 1945 at the age of seventy-eight, after spending his life doing what he wanted to do.

CHAPTER SIX

SIR HIRAM OF MAINE

And the Maxim Dynasty

Snowdrifts ten feet high were piled around a remote farm-house in Upper Abbott, Maine, one night in the late 1850's. Huddled in an old patchwork quilt beside a small kitchen fire sat Mrs. Isaac Maxim, grimly considering the family's situa-tion. The six children had gone to bed hungry. They had been hungry for three weeks. Isaac, who had lost his grist mill and made a precarious living making wooden measures, was away peddling them. When a major snowfall struck northern New England in those days, all commerce and traffic came to a halt. People stayed inside and nursed their fires, waiting to hear the bells from the ox-drawn sledges and the shouts of the rescuing snow-shovelers. Leaving his family with no money and only a little corn meal in the barrel, Isaac had planned to return in a few days with provisions. Now the strictly rationed meal was gone, and the children were chewing spruce gum to keep their jaws busy. Relatives lived not far away, but they had their own problems and the Maxims had their pride.

Early in the morning, Mrs. Maxim awoke to a muffled call. Isaac was outside, tunneling through to the door. In his sleigh were mountains of provisions. Mrs. Maxim cooked a big meal and woke up the children. They ate until they were stuffed, and Isaac, ill and exhausted, fell into bed and slept for a week.

Hunger was a routine emergency in the Maxim family, which stemmed from a tribe of tough, brawling, pioneer forebears of French and English descent. One early Maxim boasted that he had wrestled with the Devil, and according to a milder family legend, Isaac's grandmother ran and leaped over a rail fence at the age of one hundred and three.

Isaac, tall, dark, given to spells of melancholy, was born with an ax in his hands. He could run a lathe, build a wagon, invent gadgets or hoist a two-hundred-pound pork barrel, and once he beat up two highwaymen. He had never gone to school, but he learned to read and spent evenings with the Bible, ancient history, Voltaire, Tom Paine and books about Napoleon, which he took in barter on his peddling trips. But he couldn't make money. In ten years the Maxims moved eleven times. His wife Harriet, short, muscular and steely-eyed, hoed corn, milked cows, chased the bears away from the sheep, spun, wove and dyed, cured the sick with barks and herbs, bested a mad dog with her bare hands, killed stray cats to make a fur quilt, and had eight babies. When the children started to toddle, she taught them arithmetic with rows of beans on the kitchen floor. In 1843, when the Millerites, a religious group, said the world was going to end, and Isaac wanted to go to Heaven with them, she made him a white ascension robe, then jeered at him while he stood in the front yard waiting for the Resurrection.

From this stimulating background emerged a succession of world-renowned inventors, and the greatest of these was the eldest son, Hiram. He invented the Maxim gun, almost beat Edison with the electric light, built one of the first airplanes to leave the ground, and became a rich man and a British knight. His brother Hudson was a leading inventor of smokeless powder and other explosives. Brother Sam made innovations in sewing machines and other devices. Percy, Hiram's son, pioneered in early gas-buggies and invented the Maxim Silencer, and Percy's son Hamilton followed with industrial noise killers. A total of more than 370 patents have been issued to the five inventing Maxims.

The exuberant Maxim children trapped, hunted, fought, wrestled, built dams, water wheels and boats, and because of Isaac's coaching in craftsmanship, were fascinated by every tool and machine they saw. Deprived of early schooling for lack of decent clothes, they were insatiably curious about the world outside. Hudson worked in the fields for money to buy a geography book. Hiram wanted to be a sea captain. He couldn't afford a sextant, so he made one from wood and string and spent evenings shooting the North Star. Then he decided to be an artist, made colors from plants and earth, and clipped hair from the baby to make fine brushes.

At the age of fourteen Hiram was apprenticed to a Maine carriage maker, where, as he recalled later, he put in twelve hours a day making wheelbarrows, wagons, rakes and bedsteads and spent the evenings chopping wood. After six months he ran away, spent a brief period in school learning the three R's, studied astronomy in the evenings, and learned trapping and poker from the Indians. Working for another carriage maker, he developed a talent for painting bits of landscape and floral designs on sleighs and carriages, an art then highly appreciated. Somewhere in Maine today there are probably sleighs decorated by Hiram Maxim.

Hiram turned out his first invention in his father's grist mill. Mice were a problem, and the cage traps then used had to be reset after each capture. With wire from a hoopskirt, Hiram built an automatic trap which could be wound like a clock and would set itself several times, increasing the nightly catch. Then he conceived an idea of making each captive set the trap for the next mouse. The noise of the springing trap scared the mouse, which ran into a storage cage, and in so doing moved a mechanism which reset the trap.

At twenty he left Maine and became a rambling mechanic in northern New York and Canada. He had the frame of an ox, his bellow could be heard a mile, and he reveled in pranks like putting frogs in schoolmasters' water pitchers and mixing phosphorus in people's hair oil so that they glowed at night. For a short time he worked as a tavern bartender. No drinker himself, he worked out an elaborate system of thinning drinks late at night according to the customers' probable capacities, sending them home in fair shape and making money for the house.

Hiram's serious career started when he went to work in his Uncle Levi's engineering shop at Fitchburg, Massachusetts. Levi manufactured Drake's Gas Machine, which vaporized gasoline and pumped it through pipes to be burned in jets for illumination. Hiram improved the machine and was soon working in Boston for Oliver Drake, its inventor. He invented—too early to profit by it—an automatic sprinkler that would be started by the heat of a fire. Not appreciated, he went to New York, worked as a draftsman, and in his spare time devised an improved gas illuminating system. There had been trouble keeping the gas mixture even so that the lights would not go dim. This limited the number of lights that could be served by a single machine. Hiram invented a gas-density regulator and other improvements and formed the Maxim Gas Machine Company, which received big contracts. He installed his illuminating system in several New York buildings in the early 1870's, and the great day came when the fifteen hundred rooms of the Grand Union Hotel at Saratoga blazed with Maxim lights.

Hiram was now married, had two children, lived on a proper street in Brooklyn, and wore a full beard and the silk hat and frock coat of a man of position. But he couldn't be dignified. When leaving the house he always vaulted the garden gate, to the distress of his wife and the delight of his small son Hiram Percy. Life with Hiram was never dull. To prove the theory that extremes of heat and cold produce the same sensations, Hiram ostentatiously heated a poker in the kitchen range, secretly cooled another in the icebox, and tested the cool poker on the cook's neck. Mrs. Maxim had to find a new cook. Despite such heartless pranks, Hiram became furious at injustices, and when an itinerant photographer cheated another cook out of two dollars, he spent several Sundays tracking down the swindler. He found him in New Jersey, retrieved the cook's money, and had him arrested and fined. Once he passed a stockyard where the cattle were bellowing from thirst. He charged in, turned on all the faucets, and started a movement to prevent cruelty to cattle.

By this time the early electric arc lights were being used, and Edison and Swan of England were trying to perfect an incandescent electric bulb. Attempts were only partially successful because the carbon filaments burned out quickly. Hiram saw that a good bulb would put an end to his gas lights, so he found a partner, formed the United States Electric Lighting Company, and plunged into day-and-night experiments to create a durable lamp. Recalling a phenomenon he had noticed in his gaslight research, he found that if he put a little vaporized gasoline into an airtight bulb with a glowing filament, the carbon produced by the burning vapor would gather on the weak parts of the slender thread and reinforce it. This ingenious discovery greatly lengthened the bulb's life. Hiram finished his first bulb on February 7, 1880, and proudly showed that it would burn under water, a feat then considered miraculous. He did not know that Thomas

A. Edison had been granted a broad patent on the carbon-filament electric lamp eleven days before. Though hundreds of thousands of the early lamps were made by Hiram's method, he got nothing out of it. The controversy ended in a long and famous legal battle which Edison won.

Hiram remained undaunted, and all manner of original ideas poured from his fertile mind. He had trouble obtaining a rare imported chemical, phosphoric anhydride, which was used to absorb the water vapor in his bulbs. Edison had bought up the available supply. Hiram was no chemist, but in a short time he contrived a method of making the chemical cheaply in large batches. Then there was trouble with the early lighting systems because the bulbs more distant from the station were dimmer. Hiram invented a method of wiring which corrected this condition by insuring constant voltage throughout a lighting system. The new marvels of electric light excited the world, and that year, 1881, a great Electrical Exposition was held in Paris. Maxim demonstrated his new system at the show. It brought him wide acclaim, and the President of the French Republic pinned on his coat the cross of a Chevalier of the Legion of Honor.

Europe offered the forty-one-year-old Yankee Paul Bunyan new worlds to conquer. All about him he saw the need for new machines. A cynical remark made by a visitor at the Paris exhibit fired a new train of thought. "Hang your chemistry and electricity," he was told. "If you want to make a pile of money, invent something that will enable these Europeans to cut one anothers' throats with greater facility." Maxim remembered the kick of a muzzle-loading shotgun he had used as a boy, and set to work. Two years later, in 1883, he had designed the first automatic machine gun.

The machine gun, defined broadly as a rapid-fire weapon, had a long history before Hiram Maxim. The principle can be traced to about 400 B. C., when Dionysius the Tyrant invented the "polybolos" (literally, "many missiles")—an improved catapult that dispatched stones in rapid succession. And there were English archers at the Battle of Hastings who used bows designed to shoot more than one arrow at a time. In the age of explosives, the "organ gun" was the earliest rapid-fire weapon. This device was composed of a row of musket barrels mounted on a horizontal frame and either fired simultaneously or set off in rapid succession by lighting a fuse. In museums, models can be seen of organ guns invented by Leonardo da Vinci. But the great Renaissance genius was only a boy in 1467 when the Italian General Coleoni fought the battle of Piccardina with his primitive organ guns, improvised by lashing musket barrels to frames.

French gunsmiths copied Coleoni's idea, calling the weapons *ribaudequins*, "little bits of fun." The Germans grimly called them "death organs," and made them with as many as thirty-three "pipes," asserting that death played dance music on them. As recently as the American Civil War a twenty-four-barrel organ gun glared from the ramparts of a fort at Charleston, South Carolina. In World War I, French soldiers built one from captured German rifles.

Someone had to come along with the idea of bending a straight line into a circle, as Thomas Davenport did when he looked at an electromagnet that exerted linear force and thought of a rotary motor. James Puckle of London, in 1718, saw the advantage of a fast-shooting "revolver." His patent from George I gave him the exclusive right to manufacture his "portable gun or machine," similar in many ways to the modern weapon. It was mounted on a tripod and had a single barrel and a revolving series of chambers which were brought consecutively into firing position by turning a crank. By means of interchangeable parts, Mr. Puckle designed his gun to shoot square bullets as well as round ones. The round bullets, he explained soberly, were to be used "against Christians," and the square bullets "against Turks."

Puckle was ahead of his time, for the art of firearm manufacture had not progressed to the point where he could obtain suitable materials and ammunition for his gun.

Later machine-gun inventors were inspired by humanitarian motives. Dr. Richard Jordan Gatling of Indiana—whose name survives in the word "gat"—had invented machines for planting grain, and was inspired to make one that would spray bullets. His water-cooled, hand-cranked gun, which appeared in 1861, fired 350 rounds a minute. Dr. Gatling explained that fewer soldiers would be needed to shoot the same number of rounds, so the size of armies would be greatly reduced and there would be fewer casualties. Although it was successful in all tests, conservative Army heads turned the gun down. Only a few Gatling guns saw action in the Civil War, and they were purchased by the nonconformist civilian soldier General Benjamin B. Butler, who used them effectively in the campaign in Virginia. The Gatling was later used throughout the world.

Another humanitarian, Dr. J. H. McLean of St. Louis, was

building rapid-fire guns mounted on wagons at about the time
Hiram Maxim got his inspiration. He called his guns "Peace-
makers," for like Alfred Nobel, John Ericsson, and other
nineteenth century inventors of killing agents, he believed that
more deadly weapons would scare nations into ways of peace.
He cited figures to show that the introduction of the bayonet,
the percussion cap and the breechloader had resulted in reducing battle casualties.

Despite all these efforts of civilians, generals considered
the machine gun of little value when Maxim began work on
his weapon. Machine-gun units were regarded as freak ap-
pendages, and in field maneuvers, commanders often put
them on the flanks of their forces to get them out of the way.
When officers were asked to assign men for machine-gun duty,
they combed their "awkward squads."

The reader now probably knows more about the history of
the machine gun than Hiram Maxim did when he set out to
invent one. He seldom bothered to study the background of
any device. If he thought of a new machine, he quickly designed and built it and applied for patents. Many of his ap-
plications were never granted because patents already existed,
but Maxim's ignorance of his predecessors may have saved
him time in the long run, and he was spared the knowledge of
others' failures.

The rambunctious Hiram, no philosopher or humanitarian,
was simply keen on the main chance. He recalled that when
he was a boy in Maine, he and his brother Hudson had loaded
a shotgun with heavier and heavier charges in order to see
which could stand the hardest kick. His father had suggested

that instead of playing a pointless game they try to figure out a way to utilize the kick to reload the gun. This Hiram now set out to do, outlining several ways of doing the job, both by using some of the force of the expanding gas in the gun barrel and by utilizing the mechanical kick. His first English patent was granted in 1883. In Maxim's gun, the barrel and breechblock were enclosed within a frame or sleeve. The recoil pushed them back a short distance within this sleeve to actuate a mechanical device for reloading. While previous machine guns tended to jump about and were somewhat at the mercy of the individual tempo of the operator, Maxim's gun remained steady, with a great improvement in marksmanship. With its single water-cooled barrel and belt-fed cartridges, it was a model of simplicity and efficiency in its day. When the gunner held his finger on the trigger, bullets streamed out at the rate of 666 per minute.

The press and the public showed great enthusiasm over the new gun, but military men still stubbornly resisted it. Curiously enough, the gun's chief virtue, rapid fire, was deemed a vice in some quarters. American Army and Navy experts praised it highly as an interesting mechanism, but stated that its appetite for ammunition raised a serious transport problem. The Chinese took the same attitude.

But Hiram Maxim well knew that major military decisions are made by civilians. He was a master showman, and his boyish, outwardly naïve exuberance won British hearts. To British eyes, he was what a Yankee ought to be, and he showed due respect for the upper classes. He founded the Maxim Gun Company, later to become Vickers Sons & Maxim, Ltd., and set up a workshop and target range at Hatton Garden. He won the interest of the adventurous Prince of Wales, later Edward VII, who came to the range and fired the gun. There happened to be a photographer present who recorded the event. Several dukes followed suit, and soon it became the rage among the British smart set to make the pilgrimage to Hatton Garden and fire the Maxim gun. Maxim estimated that more than two hundred thousand cartridges were fired during the London social season, and he considered the money well spent.

The British government placed an order, and soon Maxim was on the road to fame and wealth. He toured Europe, easily winning competitions with other gunmakers. In one of these contests, on an Austrian target range, Emperor Franz Josef appeared unexpectedly. With great presence of mind, Maxim hung up a fresh paper target and neatly perforated it with the initials "F. J.," not forgetting the dots. The Emperor was pleased and later an order was booked. There is a story that Kaiser Wilhelm II fired the gun in person at a machine-gun competition at Spandau, Germany, that he was exhilarated to discover that he could sweep the gun like a garden hose, and that onlookers became very jittery.

The Maxim gun was first "blooded" in the British campaign in the Sudan. At the start of the African troubles, the British were using a hand-cranked machine gun. When the gunners looked over the sights at hordes of charging Africans, they sometimes got nervous and turned the cranks too fast, jamming the guns. The automatic Maxims were brought in. There was no more jamming, and the poorly armed natives were cut down in prodigious slaughter. When the troopships came home, Maxim was almost as much of a hero as Kitchener, the British commander, and at least one London journalist gave the inventor credit for winning the war. A sardonic footnote was added later by the British poet Hilaire Belloc:

"Whatever happens, we have got
The Maxim gun, and they have not."

Still the British War Office had not learned the lesson of rapid fire, and the Tommies found themselves at the wrong ends of Maxims in France in 1914. When the Kaiser first saw the gun in action, he had bought some Maxims with his own funds against the advice of his generals, and the outbreak of World War I saw the German army well equipped with Spandau-Maxims made in Germany. It is reported that the British entered the war with only two hundred machine guns. Their early casualties from machine-gun fire were heavy. It took another civilian, David Lloyd-George, to correct the costly error.

After the British peace was established in the Sudan, Queen Victoria let it be known that she regretted that Hiram Maxim was not a British subject. Maxim took the hint and was naturalized. In 1900 he was knighted. Other rulers followed suit, and soon his mighty torso was bespangled with decorations from six nations. Sir Hiram now lived at his manor house in Kent with Lady Maxim, his second wife. The first Mrs. Maxim, mother of his three children, had finally lost patience with him, and they were divorced. He was now a full-bearded gentleman of obvious importance, who wore a top hat as though born with one, but he was still a rustic prankster at heart, and his office associates often had to work overtime to protect the boss's dignity.

Years later his son Hiram Percy Maxim, in a book about his father, *A Genius in the Family*, told of a period when he disappeared mysteriously in London every evening. It was found that he had rented a room in a business building. Fearing that he was getting into some kind of trouble, his associates searched the room and found nothing but a chair, a long brass tube, and a bag of beans. Every evening the Salvation Army held a meeting across the street, and the police had received complaints that someone had been pelting them with beans. A conference was held, and Sir Hiram regretfully promised to be good.

Anyone who ever injured Sir Hiram lived to rue the day. His son recalls the almost incredible tenacity with which he tracked down two sharpers who robbed him in Paris. A deal was being consummated in which Hiram had to make payment in gold, an understandable event in the life of an international munitions peddler. Two strangers raided the office and stole the gold. Using a conventional criminal technique, one scooped the gold into a bag and ran, while the other, pretending to help, got in the way of the outraged Hiram. He called the police, canceled appointments, and spent several days without success trying to trace the thieves. He had excellent visual memory, and from that time on his eyes roamed over crowds wherever he went. Six years later in a railway station restaurant in France he recognized one of the men and tackled him at once, shouting for the police. The man escaped Hiram's clutches by slipping out of his coat and leaping on the last car of a departing train. Hiram went after him. The train entered a tunnel, and there was a savage fight in the darkness. A guard pulled the signal cord, and the train stopped. Hiram dragged the man to the ground, beat him into subjection, and turned him over to the police. Hiram had been on his way to London. He now spent several weeks in Paris and considerable money collecting evidence which led to the thief's conviction and sentence to a penal colony. Hiram filed one notch on his gun and kept his eyes open for the confederate. Seven years later he thought he saw him chatting with a pretty salesgirl in a candy booth in the Crystal Palace in London. He called Scotland Yard and spent two days with detectives watching the booth. The man finally returned. Hiram gave the signal, and the man was arrested. Once more Hiram deferred all business and pressed the case until the second man was sent to Devil's Island.

For the rest of his life Sir Hiram spent much of his time in his workshop, restlessly exploring all matters animal, vegetable and mineral. He designed a mass-production cooker to supply pork and beans to British troops and was furious when he was told that Tommies wouldn't eat the old Yankee staple.

Back in Maine when Hiram was a boy, his father Isaac had fiddled with plans for flying machines. In 1893, while on a cruise in the Mediterranean, Hiram became interested in air currents and bird flights and went home with plans to put man in the air. Using surprisingly precocious concepts, he built experimental wings and propellers and tested them on a spinning turntable which served as a kind of wind tunnel.

He built the lightest steam engine possible and assembled his plane on a forty-acre field, with steel launching tracks and a tethering device for limiting flight tests. On a trial run it bounded forward, rose from the tracks and broke loose, and for a brief moment Sir Hiram was airborne. Then a propeller hit an object, the machine was wrecked, and he abandoned the costly project. Many people believe that he was on the way toward building a workable plane, but that some of his ideas were unsound. Later the Wright brothers profited by his detailed reports.

During the thirty years of Hiram Maxim's greatest productivity, hardly a year elapsed in which he was not granted several patents either in England or the United States. The diversity of his interests and the speed with which he translated his ideas into working devices was amazing. His first patented invention, in 1866, was an improved iron for curling hair. Among his other inventions were carburetors, meters, pumps, chandeliers, motor governors, stonecutting machines, vacuum cleaners, ship stabilizers, railway wheels, pneumatic tires, fire extinguishers, an improved blackboard, a compressed air gun for torpedoes, riveting machines and coffee substitutes. He was also a pioneer in the field of explosive mixtures and smokeless powders.

In 1912, after a study of the guidance mechanism of bats, he suggested a subsonic siren for ships by which they could locate surrounding objects by echoes, like the sonar system now used by submarines. He died in 1916 at the age of seventy-six, soon after patenting a process for cracking heavy oils to make gasoline—a technique indispensable in providing fuel for today's automobiles.

Sir Hiram was dead, but Isaac of Maine had founded a dynasty of inventors, and the Maxim genius marched on. Three of the brothers had died early, two of them in the Civil War. Sam stayed on the farm, patented oil lamps, ironing boards and sewing-machine improvements, and read to the family in the evenings. Hudson, the sixth child, who had changed his name from Isaac, grew up like Hiram with bulging muscles, a fearless disposition, and a burning passion for knowledge and adventure. At fifteen he was walking miles through snowdrifts to district schools and throwing all comers in wrestling matches at county fairs. Hiram asked him to come to New York and help him with his gas machines. Hudson arrived in a lumberman's shirt and a knitted cap made by his mother. A circus bought one of Hiram's lighting systems, and Hudson traveled with the show to operate it. He loved to ride in the parade, wearing armor and a plumed helmet. He invaded New York's Houston Street wrestling section, called "Murderers' Row," and threw several pros. A promoter tried to sign him up, but he wanted more schooling and returned to Maine. There he enrolled in a boarding school, working in a quarry and selling books to pay expenses. After he finished school, he was offered a teaching vacancy on the condition that he take care of a tough boy who had thrown the latest incumbent out the window. Hudson won the decision in one round, and the job was his.

Soon Hudson and a crippled schoolmate named Alden

Knowles formed a partnership for the simple purpose of making money. Knowles made ink from an old recipe, and Hudson read medical books and brewed a concoction, composed mostly of kerosene and camphor, which he labeled "Maxim's Lightning Cure—Good for What Ails You." They bought a peddler's cart and a horse named Bucephalus and set off to sell their ink and tonic through remote areas of Connecticut, Pennsylvania and Ohio. Hudson also gave lectures on phrenology, and Knowles, an expert penman, produced an instruction manual for the florid calligraphy of the day which they sold for fifty cents a copy. They lived from hand to mouth until Hudson got the bright idea of a powdered ink to be sold in capsules. Made in several colors, it could be dissolved in water to make writing fluids. The capsules sold well, and they launched a prosperous mail-order business.

Hudson opened a publishing firm and explored various other callings, but he was never quite happy until he began experimenting with deadly mixtures which went off with a loud bang. He worked for Hiram in England for a time, found the same hemisphere too small for them, and came home with samples of foreign gunpowders. He discovered a rotting shack near the Hoosac Tunnel in western Massachusetts, where explosives had been stored, and collected driblets of nitroglycerin from old tin cans for his experiments. After he married and moved to Brooklyn, things sometimes went off in his backyard laboratory. To prove that explosives were harmless if handled correctly, he would light his cigar with a stick of dynamite and burn nitroglycerin to heat a chafing dish. The neighbors still were doubtful.

Needing more room for his violent pets, Hudson took over a small plant in a deserted area of New Jersey, which he later renamed Maxim. There explosions were commonplace, as he tested all manner of mixtures. Once he was careless, and his left hand was blown off. Assaulted by a ruffian a few weeks later, he knocked him out with his right.

Hudson invented and patented several new and more powerful explosives and became recognized as a leading authority. The invention that made him famous was the perfection of an efficient smokeless powder for large guns. The stick of smokeless powder then used could not push the projectile from the barrel fast enough, because it lacked the burning surface needed to maintain high pressure as the projectile moved forward and made more room in the barrel. Mixing explosive cakes of various kinds, Hudson put holes in them to make them burn faster. His perforated powder sticks were adopted by the Army and Navy. The du Pont Company bought Hudson's patents and hired him as consultant, and he continued to make profitable loud noises.

During World War I Hudson was chairman of the committee on ordnance and explosives of the Naval Consulting Board, examining thousands of inventions submitted to the Navy. He was himself granted seventy-four patents for explosives and machines to make them, for torpedoes, time fuses, a steam cooker and a road-building machine. As early as 1875 Hudson had written a speculative paper, "Principles of Force and Demonstration of the Existence of the Atom," in which he postulated the compound nature of the atom. He speculated about solar power, proposed the heated pave-

ments now in use to melt snow, and suggested the distant showing of Broadway plays by something he called "teleview." As
a schoolboy he had memorized Pope's "Essay on Man" and
all his life recited long passages. Once in a public debate he
was preceded by an opponent whose arguments were sense-
less, but whose delivery was impressive. In Hiram's rebuttal,
he convulsed the audience by running the complete gamut of
emotions while repeating the vowels, a, e, i, o, u.

Late in their lives, Hiram was always accusing Hudson of
stealing his inventions, and the heavy-hitting Maxims, both
masters of invective and abuse, hammered at each other in
technical papers to everyone's entertainment, including their
own.

Not to be outdone by Sir Hiram, Hudson built a rambling
castle on the shore of Lake Hopatcong, New Jersey, and became an eccentric lord of the manor, entertaining everyone
who liked baked beans. At seventy he used to jump over the
net after a fast game of tennis. He like to play King Neptune
in the Atlantic City beauty pageants, riding on a float with
crown, trident and flowing white beard. Shortly before he
died, in 1927, he told his doctor that he, not Einstein, had
discovered the theory of relativity.

One day in 1894, while the wild brothers were cavorting
across the front pages of newspapers, a crowd gathered in
Lynn, Massachusetts, to see a studious young man named
Hiram Percy Maxim ride a weird, sputtering vehicle down a
hill. The motor-driven tricycle collapsed, threw its inventor
and died in the gutter. A Boston upbringing and an M. I. T.
education had combed the Maxim burrs out of old Hiram's

son Percy, but in mechanical enterprise he was a chip off the old block. A cyclist, he thought it would be a simple matter to build a small gasoline motor to push the pedals for him. The crude motor he constructed was so heavy that three wheels were needed to support it. Soon he was mounting his engines in buggies. Haynes, Winton, Ford and many others were similarly engaged, but Percy hadn't heard of them. Nor had he heard of a gearshift, a differential, a spark plug or a cooling system; he counted on taking care of such minor details on a dull afternoon in the electrical shop where he worked.

One of the few men who did not think Percy crazy was Colonel Albert A. Pope, Hartford bicycle manufacturer. He hired him to develop a practical motor vehicle. Fashioning and refashioning by trial and error the many ingenious automobile parts which we now take for granted, Percy assembled his gas-buggies and tested them over rutty roads, carrying tools and spare parts and a chart showing the location of blacksmith shops. By a miracle of imaginative craftsmanship, he turned out within four years a car that ran from Hartford to Boston and back and beat a Stanley Steamer in a race. Soon Pope was leading the country in the building of motor carriages, both gasoline and electric. The first city taxicab fleets were composed of Maxim-designed electric vehicles.

When the pioneer work was done, big business moved in, and Percy Maxim was not dealt into the game. He was casting about for new worlds to conquer when a friend made a suggestion. Hiram had invented rapid-fire guns and Hudson had eliminated the smoke which betrayed their position. Why not complete the job by silencing the guns, so that the enemy would have no clue to the origin of projectiles? This seemed fantastic, but Percy thought it over. Like Archimedes, he found the answer in his bathtub. The whirling motion of water going down the drain suggested a spiral gadget to whirl the gases leaving a gun barrel, slowing them down and killing the noise. This was the origin of the world-famous Maxim silencer. The gun-silencer was never a commercial success; military men considered it impractical and civil authorities banned it as an aid to criminals. But it made its inventor a pioneer in the important new business of killing nerve-shattering industrial noises.

About this time Percy's son Hiram Hamilton finished at M. I. T. and joined forces with his father. In the 1920's the highly efficient oil-burning diesel engine was being adapted for cargo vessels, but the noise of the exhaust was unbearable. The Maxims invented big cylinders containing sound traps which were attached to the exhaust pipes. They were widely adopted. Percy died in 1936, and Hamilton carried on the work. More than half the vessels in America's World War II navy were diesel-powered, and nine out of ten of them were quieted by Maxim silencers. Without these devices, troops on landing craft could not have heard orders above the din, and surfacing submarines would have announced their presence to craft miles away. In the early days of jet engines, their terrific roar on the testing stands made factory workers sick. Now Maxim silencers have cut the shout to a whisper.

Private diesel-electric plants in many large hospitals, department stores and office buildings run quietly because of the work of Percy and Hamilton. During the war, automatic cannons equipped with Maxim silencers were tried out in the basement of the Colt factory in Hartford without disturbing the general manager, whose office was directly overhead. Hamilton has also worked on improved snow-moving equipment, and to clear his driveway in Farmington, Connecticut, built a light V-shaped plow which he attached to the bumper of his car. A genuine Maxim, he made and sold several thousand of them.

All these ideas must have appealed to old Isaac, gazing down from his celestial workbench at the breed of men he sired.

CHAPTER SEVEN

NIKOLA TESLA

Genius of Electric Power

"Talent is that which is in a man's power; genius is that in whose power a man is," wrote James Russell Lowell. "Genius," a badly debased word, can be applied without hesitation to Nikola Tesla, by Lowell's definition or any other. The intense, arrogant Serbian, whose chief memorial is the world's electric power system, was born with strange transcendent gifts, and his dramatic bursts of discovery reminded his awed admirers of Plato's concept of a guardian daemon who directs the hand and mind of a chosen mortal.

For example, there was the famous scene in a park in Budapest on a February afternoon in 1882. The twenty-five-year-old Tesla, six-foot-two in height, with coal-black hair and gray-blue eyes burning in a long, gaunt face, was strolling with a friend. An engineer in the new Budapest telephone system in the daytime and an inventor of electrical devices at night, he had finally collapsed and was emerging from a serious breakdown. His friend Szigeti, an athlete, was coaching him back to health.

The sunset was spectacular, and the two men stopped to admire it. Tesla recited an apt passage from Goethe's *Faust*, which he knew by heart. Suddenly he stopped and stared like a man who saw a blinding vision.

"I've got it!" he announced. "After six years, I've got it. It is running at last! See! I throw the switch and reverse it. It runs either way. And it doesn't spark, for there is no commutator. It doesn't need one."

Gazing at something he saw as clearly as others saw the grass and trees, he picked up a stick and drew a diagram in the dust. This was for his friend; Tesla never needed diagrams. What he drew was a rough sketch of the alternating-current induction motor which was soon to revolutionize the production and transmission of electric power. As a student he had discovered the great need for such a motor and had pondered the problem endlessly with no apparent success. Now it had come unbidden and stood complete and perfect in his mind. Pointing with his stick, he "ran" his motor, while his friend looked on with slowly dawning comprehension. To Nikola Tesla, the motor already existed; nothing remained but to translate it into metal.

Six years later Tesla read an epochal paper to the Ameri-

can Institute of Electrical Engineers in New York and showed
to the world the picture that he had drawn in the sand. His
announcement struck the shackles from electric power and
launched today's industrial civilization. The few direct-current plants then in use could send their power only a half-
mile or so, but Tesla's discovery of the "rotating magnetic
field," the principle of his induction motor, ushered in the
era of power transmission over hundreds of miles by means of
alternating current.

Without this invention today's great networks of power
lines would not exist. Throttled by the limitations of direct
current, a city like New York or Chicago would need thousands of small plants to provide the equivalent of today's
service. Small manufacturers would be hampered by the
cost of making their own power. There would be no Tennessee
Valley Authority power system, no Bonneville Dam, no rural
electrification program. Farmers without private power plants
would still use kerosene lamps, and lack of electricity would
limit food production on millions of acres. Only a small
fraction of homes could afford electric light and power devices.
It is true that other scientists were advancing toward the same
goal and very likely would have arrived at similar conclusions
sooner or later, but Nikola Tesla was the first to see the system complete and to understand its importance.

Tesla really "saw" his motor in the park that day, it seems.
He had an uncanny knack of vivid and exact visualization
which caused him great secret agony as a boy. He sometimes
confused the scenes which appeared on his mental picture
screen with reality. Sometimes the images would not dis-

appear. Frightened, he consulted his mother, who encouraged him to summon up other images to block them out. As a result of this vigorous self-discipline, he developed a "camera mind." In classes in mathematics, at which he excelled, he found that he did not need a blackboard to work out a problem. He could work faster on his mental blackboard, where long operations in algebra appeared at lightning speed and remained indelible until he willed them away. Since his answers were always correct, teachers sometimes thought he was cheating.

Tesla was born in 1856 in the village of Smiljan, in what is now Yugoslavia. Overshadowed in boyhood by a gifted brother who died young, he strove mightily to excel in all fields. His father, a clergyman, was determined that Nikola follow in his path, but his mother, an amateur inventor like her father, became the boy's inspiration. She could not read or write, but she had devised looms, churns and other household and farm tools, and all his life Tesla boasted that she could tie three knots in an eyelash.

Like many distinguished scientists, Tesla first demonstrated his natural bent by a fondness for mechanical gadgets and by his originality in constructing them. He built his first "engine" as a small boy by gluing sixteen June bugs to the arms of a windmill-like device. They spun the arms rapidly when they flew. Using thread for a belt, he geared the engine to a flywheel and was amazed at the torque (turning power) the device produced. He planned a hundred-bug-power engine, but turned to other wonders. He found that when he breathed deeply he achieved a sensation of lightness (caused by overventilation of the lungs) and believed that he could learn to fly, like the birds he watched. After long breathing practice he took a large umbrella to a barn roof, inhaled deeply, and jumped off. Because of insufficient research, he spent several weeks in bed, but insisted that some day men would fly at a thousand miles an hour. He built a popgun from cane, learned how to make more powerful ones, and went into the business of manufacturing them for his friends. Windows were broken, and he was forced to close shop. He read omnivorously, sometimes all night. His father hid the candles, so he built a mold and made his own candles.

When Tesla was seven, his father took a church in the city of Gospic. The boy missed the animals, birds and mountains of rural Smiljan and was ill at ease with his urbane schoolmates. Soon, however, he became a local hero. A new fire company was organized, with a fine new pump operated by sixteen men. There was a dedication with a suitable parade and speeches. The order was given to start the pump. The uniformed stalwarts, eight to a side, moved the horizontal pump bars up and down, but no water came and it was most embarrassing. Nikola had never seen a fire pump, but visualized its mechanism in a flash, tore off his clothes and jumped in the river. He found the kink in the suction hose he was looking for and straightened it out. Water spurted from the pump, and the day was saved. Firemen hoisted Nikola to their shoulders and the crowd cheered.

Fascinated by the power of falling water, he built a series of water wheels. He saw a picture of Niagara Falls and announced that some day he would harness it. Once when he was

swimming in a mill pond, he was carried against the wall of
the dam, and the pressure of the water was slowly crushing
him. In his extremity there flashed into his mind a school-
book diagram showing that the pressure of a moving fluid is
proportional to the area exposed, so he turned on his side,
reducing the pressure, and managed to crawl to safety. He
built a kind of engine based on a vacuum at one end of a free
cylinder, while he alternated the air pressure at the other end,
but found he couldn't maintain the vacuum.

Tesla's vaulting ambition was geared to a frail physique,
and during his adolescence he had several crackups which
he barely survived. During one bout of illness he lost all desire to live. Then he picked up an early book by Mark Twain,
which convinced him that life held possibilities. Years later,
he told the story to his friend Mr. Clemens, who was deeply
moved.

Sent away to school at Carlstadt, Croatia, he lived with
a grim aunt who believed that delicate boys should not eat too
much, and he nearly starved. The swamps of the area were
mosquito-infested. He got malaria and was always full of
quinine. While in this precarious condition he saw a classroom electrical device which determined his career. His ingenious professor of physics had built a machine in which a
pivoted bulb coated with tinfoil was made to spin when connected to a static machine. The impact of this demonstration
on Tesla was similar to Thomas Davenport's great vision of
power when he saw Henry's electromagnet. He felt that he
would die if he did not know more about this mysterious and

wonderful phenomenon. But his parents still insisted that he must enter the clergy, and he saw no other choice.

He returned to Gospic on vacation. Just before he left he received a letter from his father suggesting that he go on a hunting trip instead. He had little heart for the sport and disregarded the offer. When he reached home he found that cholera was raging in Gospic—his father had tried to protect him. Cholera was then thought to be transmitted through the air. Tesla drank the untreated water like everyone else and contracted an almost fatal case.

The end seemed near. His father sat by his side. "Perhaps I will recover," said Nikola, "if you let me study electrical engineering."

"You will go to the best technical institution I can find," his father promised. A great weight rolled from the boy's mind. He smiled and drifted into an easy sleep. His recovery astonished the doctors.

At his father's request, he spent a year in the mountains on the deferred hunting trip to regain his health. He was no menace to wildlife, for he smuggled along a bag of books and strode through the hills allowing his kaleidoscopic mind to present an endless variety of fantastic inventions. One of his visions was a submarine tube across the Atlantic through which containers of letters would be dispatched by water pressure. He made many mental calculations, but learned later that it would be impossible to maintain the pressure because of the friction of the water on the tube's wall. He conjured up Jovian schemes for harnessing the power of the earth's rotation to run man's machines, and dreamed of a global transportation system involving a free-floating ring high above the Equator, whose speed could be regulated— a kind of celestial moving sidewalk. In an age when we are seriously considering multi-billion-dollar sky platforms, Tesla's early schemes seem less grandiose. Even his more preposterous notions were of value in his training. They encouraged both audacity and a will to work until he encountered limitations.

At nineteen, Tesla entered technical school at Gratz, Austria. It was like releasing an arrow from a bow. Anxious to prove to his parents that the choice was wise, he worked for long stretches from three in the morning until eleven at night. A professor urged his father to take him home before he killed himself.

Electricity, then an almost unexplored wilderness, fascinated him. In his second year at Gratz an incident took place which gave focus to his bursting energy. One of his professors demonstrated to the class a direct-current Gramme motor just received from Paris. It was sparking badly, and Tesla wondered how this could be prevented.

Any electric motor is, essentially, an arrangement of magnets which alternately attract and repel one another in such a way that rotary motion is created. As Davenport discovered in 1834, a simple model can be made by drilling a hole in the center of a straight bar magnet and mounting it on a pin between the poles of a horseshoe electromagnet. The north pole of the bar magnet spins around to the south pole of the fixed magnet. There it would stop were it not for the commutator, a metal spring connection which reverses the poles of the electromagnet, thus giving the revolving part another kick and creating the rotary motion which runs machines.

In the motor Tesla saw, it was the brush commutator which was sparking. Tesla suggested that a motor might be built without a commutator, so there would be no contact between the circular rotating part and the fixed poles whose magnetic attraction pulled it around. Such a motor would not spark and would be simpler to operate, he said. And it would work on alternating current, which reverses direction periodically, instead of the direct current which travels in a steady stream. Not even Tesla could then perceive the full importance of that fact.

Tesla's idea stirred up a classroom controversy, and Professor Poeschl patiently demolished his plan. "Mr. Tesla may accomplish great things," he conceded, "but he certainly will never do this. It is a perpetual motion scheme, an impossible idea." Few scientists then living would have disputed Poeschl, but his rebuff did not penetrate. Tesla's mind could not detach itself from the problem. When he spoke up in class he had no idea how a motor could be built without a commutator, but he knew there ought to be one, and he was determined to build it. For six years his mind filed away pertinent data. The cerebral motors when he "tested" were so real to him that he could hear the whir, smell the lubricating oil, and detect signs of wear.

Leaving Gratz, he spent a year in an engineering job, then went to the University of Prague to complete his studies. Everywhere he went, the invisible motor went with him. Disturbed by his pallor, his classmates urged him to join them now and then in a carefree evening, and he developed a fondness for billiards and cards. He usually won at cards, but on one disastrous evening lost his year's expenses. Expecting to leave school, he explained the situation to his mother. She did not complain, and advanced more money. Back at school, he recouped his losses in an all-night game and never gambled again.

After a year at Prague, he decided to support himself and took a job with the Budapest telephone company, spending nights on his motor. Working around the clock brought on a nervous breakdown. If he passed under a bridge, he felt a crushing pressure on his skull. A shaft of sunlight was like a physical blow. He was annoyed at the ticking of a watch three rooms from his and complained of the dull thud of flies alighting on the table. He had a compulsion to count his steps, and he could not eat without first estimating the cubic volume of the dishes. The athlete Szigeti took him in hand. Then came the sudden, triumphant vision in the park, when all the parts of his motor fell magically into place.

Tesla had accomplished a tremendous feat of intuitive imagination. Throwing away the commutator in his mind and persistently exploring every hunch, he had finally found a way to keep the wheel spinning without the current-reversing mechanism. By means of an elaborate wiring system, he worked out a method of sending a wave of alternating current around the outside of the wheel so that the magnetic attraction constantly rotated, pulling the wheel around, somewhat as a mechanical rabbit lures the whippets around a racetrack.

But single-phase a.c. motors have serious limitations, as other inventors had discovered. To the revolving lure Tesla added a second wave of alternating current which broke step with the first. Then he added a third. This was like adding more cylinders to an engine. In effect, it made three motors out of one. This was the origin of "polyphase transmission," a flexible system which plays a great and indispensable role in modern industry. Today it is common practice to use a three-phase motor to run three separate lighting circuits, or all three circuits may be combined to yield a great increase of power. There are few direct-current motors larger than two hundred horsepower, but the Tesla polyphase a.c. motors are built to yield forty thousand or better, and there is no known limit to their size.

After recovering from his breakdown, Tesla became an expert trouble-shooter for ailing power and light plants, with headquarters in Paris. While riding on trains in apparent idleness, he was mentally devising new forms of his induction motor and trying it out for various uses. Finally when stationed in Strasbourg, Alsace, he bought materials, rented space in a machine shop, and built his first motor. He was not surprised when it ran.

This was only the beginning, for Tesla was in the process of designing, not simply a motor, but an entirely new electric power system. This required generators to produce a.c. power, a wide variety of a.c. motors to use it for various purposes, transformers to step down the voltage from the power lines, and many other devices which the new concept demanded.

He tried to find backers, but European industrialists were skeptical. He fell in with a group of American engineers, with whom he played billiards. One of them, Charles Bachellor, urged him to go to New York and work for his boss, Thomas Edison. Tesla accepted at once and bought transportation. Racing for the boat train at Paris, he found that his tickets and money were gone. He talked his way across the Atlantic and landed at the Battery with four cents, some poems he had written, plans for a flying machine, and a letter to Edison.

The day after he landed, Tesla went to work for Edison, whose Pearl Street plant, opened two years before, was then lighting a few hundred New York buildings. Edison, a plain, self-trained man, could be grumpily suspicious of formal education and culture. He had reservations about this hand-some, volatile European with his superior manner, and he gave him some greasy jobs. Late one afternoon he sent him to inspect the lighting system on the steamship *Oregon*, the fastest liner afloat. It had broken down, sailing was delayed, and the dynamos could not be replaced because the ship had, in effect, been built around them. Tesla quickly diagnosed the trouble and with the help of the crew spent the night putting the system in order. At five the next morning Edison and his men, homeward bound on Fifth Avenue after a night's work, met the debonair Tesla.

"Our Parisian friend has been enjoying night life," re-marked Edison coolly, and asked him for his report. "Mr. Edison," said Tesla, "I have just finished on the *Oregon*.

The lights are working." Edison looked at him curiously and walked off. "He must be a damn good man," he said later.

Their association was brief. Tesla studied Edison's d.c. dynamos and saw many ways in which they could be improved. Edison told him to go ahead, tossing off some phrase like "There's fifty thousand dollars in it if you can do it." We are told that this was a stock witticism of the period. Tesla spent months designing new dynamos which, when tested, showed the advantages he promised. Then he asked for his bonus and was told that he did not understand American humor. Money is no joking matter to Europeans, and Tesla resigned. For the rest of his life he loathed the name of Edison.

A lean period followed. He worked on arc lights for a time and was paid in worthless stock. He was reduced to ditch-digging. He resented this waste of time, all the more so because he was working for Edison's lighting company. Then he enlisted the aid of A. K. Brown of the Western Union Telegraph Company, who became a convert to his a.c. system. He and a friend financed the Tesla Electric Company. In a laboratory not far from Edison's, on South Fifth Avenue (now called West Broadway), Tesla happily set to work building prototypes of his alternating-current generators and the motors and transformers needed to use the new kind of power. He sent a motor to Professor W. A. Anthony of Cornell, a leading authority, who tested it and made a glowing report. Tesla applied for a string of patents, and as they were issued, the technical world woke up. He was invited to read a paper before the American Institute of Electrical Engineers. Delivered on May 16, 1888, the paper shook the young electrical industry to its foundations. Within a month, far-sighted George Westinghouse paid Tesla's company a million dollars for the patent rights and hired Tesla to come to Pittsburgh and supervise the construction of the new equipment.

There was a mighty furor. Almost no one shared the conviction of Tesla and Westinghouse that alternating current was the key to electric power development, and many important apple carts would be upset if they succeeded. Few engineers had ever used a.c., and it was universally distrusted because of the high voltage generated. Pointing out that it was used in the new electric chair, opponents speciously argued that it would be a public menace if sent over power lines. It has even been suggested that the death chair was developed as a propaganda weapon in "the battle of the currents."

Tesla countered dramatically by passing a million volts harmlessly through his body. This also had little to do with the case, since he used extremely high frequencies which travel over the surface and do not penetrate, but it was a wonderful show. It was whispered about that this saturnine genius possessed some sort of magic immunity.

Edison, smarting because he had nourished the Balkan rebel, fought furiously to prevent the adoption of his system and tried to secure legislation to outlaw it. He might as well have campaigned against the automobile. Because of the strong current necessary for d.c. transmission, heat losses drastically limited the distance over which power could be sent without increasing the gauge of the wire to impractical diameters. In fact, there is not enough copper in the world to convert the American power system to direct current. The high voltages and the correspondingly weaker current possible with the use of a.c. clearly indicated the solution. And Tesla's inventions gave the world the tools needed to apply this fact. Other inventors contested his patents, particularly Galileo Ferraris of Italy, but after long litigation the courts sustained all of Tesla's claims.

Tesla's first great public triumph came in 1893 when the Chicago World's Fair, the first world's fair to be lighted by electricity, was gorgeously illuminated by 92,622 bulbs powered by twelve of Tesla's polyphase a.c. generators. And in the Electrical Building, Nikola Tesla himself, suitably illuminated by fifteen thousand bulbs, dazzled the multitude with an exhibition of "scientific magic." Three years later the foes of alternating current were finally silenced when the lights went on in Buffalo, twenty-five miles from the giant new Westinghouse generators at Niagara Falls. Tesla had definitely arrived.

Tesla did not stay long with Westinghouse. He was not cut out to be an employee. He was impatient with slow thinkers, and he was always pulling blueprints out of his mental filing cabinet which baffled his more systematic colleagues. Now comparatively wealthy from the sale of his patents, he plunged into numerous projects in his New York laboratory.

He became a fastidious man of fashion, a man of mystery and something of a social lion. By rigorous exercise he had conquered his boyhood frailty, and now he ruled his living with a will of iron. He regarded himself as a fine precision in-

strument, and to maintain it in top form he denied himself
many of the customary consolations of the male. As a student
he was an incessant cigar smoker, but had severed the habit
with one blow. He even believed that gumchewing damaged
the system. He distrusted and avoided women and hoped for
a millennium of "desexualized workers" who would be sustained by love of work alone. There is a legend that Sarah
Bernhardt dropped her handkerchief near him and that he
returned it without a word.

He had one elegant indulgence. Every night at eight he
appeared in evening clothes at Delmonico's or the Waldorf.
Towering, impressive, aloof, he was conducted to his personal
table. Beside his plate was a stack of napkins. The head-
waiter retained his composure while Tesla thoroughly wiped
his dinner service and, when he entertained, those of his
guests. He ordered elaborate meals, cooked by his own recipes
and accompanied by fine wines. He sampled each dish before
allowing his guests to be served and often sent one back
because the sauce lacked the precise nuance that he demanded.
Rising from the table exactly at ten, he went to his laboratory
to work the night through.

Tesla's fame was now world-wide, and the world's leading
scientists flocked to his lectures here and abroad. He enjoyed
giving private showings of new electrical discoveries, and in-
vitations were highly prized by prominent New Yorkers. He
knew the elder J. P. Morgan. He experimented with electrical
illumination by means of gas-filled tubes—the precursors of
today's neon and fluorescent lamps—and waved the glass
wands like swords of fire in the dark laboratory, looking like

Count Dracula. He also discovered the heating effect of short-wave currents on the human body, gave himself "electrical baths" with them, and suggested, long before diathermy therapy came into practice, that they might be used in treating various diseases.

In 1893 Tesla became the first to announce the principle of radio tuning, so christened by him because he compared it to the sympathetic vibration of a tuning fork with another fork of the same pitch. After conducting successful tests in wireless transmission by means of a high-frequency a.c. generator, he outlined a world-wide broadcasting system of news bulletins, music, stock prices and correct time, available to anyone by means of a cheap and simple receiving set. He also predicted the broadcasting of photographs and drawings. While he was in the middle of this work, his laboratory burned down, destroying the equipment on which he had spent most of his money. This was a bitter blow, but he secured fresh capital and resumed his experiments.

When on Christmas Eve, 1906, Reginald Fessenden, radio pioneer, broadcast music to ships at sea from his station at Brant Rock, Massachusetts, a giant generator such as Tesla had built was used to broadcast the signals. Ernst F. W. Alexanderson, the noted engineer who built the Brant Rock generator, stated: "In almost every step of progress in electrical power engineering, as well as in radio, we can trace the spark of thought back to Nikola Tesla." Although today's radio men state that Tesla's approach was erroneous, the late Edwin H. Armstrong, famous for his inventions in radio, once said that if Tesla had followed up his original broadcasting experiments, there was a good possibility that he would have found the right track, and Armstrong blamed himself and other scientists for "failing completely to realize the significance of Tesla's words."

Tesla was too impatient to stick with one idea until its commercial possibilities were fully developed. With amazing intuition he pointed the way for others and dashed on to new fields. One of his most spectacular inventions was a device called the Tesla Coil, which could produce high frequencies for experimental use. It could also emit dazzling displays of artificial lightning, and physics teachers throughout the world have been demonstrating it to their classes for half a century. Broadcasting antennas and automobile ignition systems are elaborations of that device. He also invented an ingenious automobile speedometer which operated by air friction. It was manufactured for many years, to be superseded by today's speedometer, which is based on another Tesla invention, the induction motor. Long before Fritz Haber of Germany perfected his method of extracting nitrogen from the air for making explosives and fertilizer—thereby enabling Germany to launch World War I—Tesla did a long series of experiments on the project and accurately predicted the value of these synthetic fertilizers in increasing food production.

In 1898 a weird craft appeared in the sea off New York. There was no one aboard, yet it dashed about in intricate patterns as though responding to human directions. This was Tesla's radio-controlled boat, with which he pioneered in the field of remotely controlled planes, craft and missiles. He proposed a radio-directed rocket and predicted such weapons of unlimited range against which no city could save itself. Long ago he warned that the release of the energy in the atom might bring disaster to mankind.

One of the great goals of Tesla's later life was the wireless transmission of electric power. Backed by John Jacob Astor, he built a mysterious laboratory in the Colorado mountains to test his plan. His theory was complex, but in brief, he believed it possible to charge the earth with electrical energy which could be tapped with suitable apparatus at distant points. No complete record of these experiments exists, but it was reported that he succeeded in lighting lamps and running small motors more than fifteen miles from the laboratory. In 1902, with the backing of J. P. Morgan, he began building a fantastic 150-foot tower at Shoreham, Long Island, which was intended as a great station for radio broadcasting and the transmission of power by wireless. Because of contractors' delays and financial difficulties, the station was never completed. There have been many auditorium demonstrations of the broadcasting of electric power over short distances to light up bulbs and tubes. Since, like light rays, these electromagnetic radiations dissipate their power proportionately to the square of the distance transmitted, the commercial broadcasting of power is held to be impractical. Barring new evidence, it is safe to dismiss Tesla's plan as one of his less fortunate inspirations.

As the decades rolled by Tesla became a hotel recluse, noted for his many eccentricities. Money was never important to him except as raw material for experiments. He poured out his gifts and expected that somehow he would be provided for. He lived on a pension granted him by the Yugoslavian government, plus an occasional check for a popular magazine article. He followed a fastidious regime in the hope of living to be a hundred and fifty. In the winter he seldom left his single room, which he kept at a temperature of ninety degrees, with the doors and windows taped to keep out fresh air. He lived mainly on milk and vegetables, and every day he sent a special Western Union boy to the market for them. The vegetables were boiled for two hours, and only two chefs were entrusted with their preparation.

Every July tenth he gave a birthday party for newspapermen, serving them Scotch while he sipped boiled milk and reported the results of his year's thinking. Year by year his predictions became more vague and lurid. He talked of harnessing "cosmic force," and of rays that would kill men by the million and immobilize airplane engines hundreds of miles away. A reporter leaving one of these parties was heard to mutter, "If anyone but Tesla had said that, I'd say he was crazy." Others were not as charitable. Yet Tesla's genius had changed the face of the world, and even in his dotage manufacturers were uneasy lest machines worth billions should be made obsolete by a final stroke of Tesla intuition. He was found dead in his room on January 7, 1943, when he was eighty-six. Behind him he left a great mass of findings and conjectures which have yet to be sifted and weighed. We may not have heard the last of Tesla.

At the close of a stern life almost barren of love or affection, he was overcome by a touching devotion to pigeons. For years the gaunt, silent man in black, with his bag of bird food, was a familiar sight in Bryant Park near the New York Public Library or on the steps of St. Patrick's Cathedral a few blocks away. When he could no longer go out, he sent his messenger to find ailing pigeons and nursed them to health in his room, stroking and admiring them for hours. The key may be found in his childhood. When he was six, and his family moved from their rural village, the boy's beloved pigeons were left behind. He was inconsolable. Soon he was caught up by ambition. Now, after many years, he had found his pigeons.

A. Ravielli

CHAPTER EIGHT

LEE DE FOREST

Father of Radio

In a Federal courtroom in New York in December, 1913, a sardonic prosecuting attorney confronted a lean, shabby, badgered inventor who had been brought into court with his colleagues on criminal charges of using the mails to defraud.

The prosecutor gingerly held before the jury a glass object which looked like a small light bulb with wires protruding from the top. With masterly scorn and ridicule he explained that the defendant, Lee de Forest, had, over his own signature, made "absurd and deliberately misleading statements" that by means of this device the human voice would some day be transmitted across the Atlantic Ocean. Because of such preposterous claims, gullible investors had been persuaded to pay as much as ten or twenty dollars a share for stock in de Forest's company, he said, and urged the jury in the name of the people of the United States to mete out to this man and his partners the penalty they richly deserved—terms in the Atlanta Penitentiary.

Two of de Forest's associates were convicted, but he was acquitted with a severe lecture from the judge, who advised him to abandon all pretense of being an inventor and to find an ordinary job and stick to it.

That "worthless glass bulb" which almost sent Lee de Forest to prison was the audion tube, which has since been rated as the greatest single invention of the twentieth century and one of the few truly original devices ever conceived by the mind of man. It was the foundation of the entire electronics industry. It made possible the loud-speaker, ocean-spanning phone calls, the transmission of news photos by wire and radio, talking pictures, radar, and many other electronic devices that are saving hundreds of millions of dollars a year in industry. The audion tube belongs near the top of any list of man's inventions that have remade the world.

The fragile bulb certainly looked unimportant, and it is not surprising that laymen had no idea how it was supposed to work. Not even de Forest, a staunch believer in his genius, had a full appreciation of the magnitude of his discovery. But he did foresee that the tube would control electric power, delicately, accurately, and with incredible speed. By means of the curious arrangement of wires and plates bunched inside the bulb, it would detect a feeble whisper of the air waves and enable local power to amplify it into a shout that could be heard round the world. The tube was an Aladdin's lamp that gave to the tiny electron the power of a mighty genie.

Less than two years after the crumpled inventor had left the courtroom, his audion tube had done what he claimed it would do—it had carried the human voice across the Atlantic Ocean. At the same time, the first regular telephone service from New York to San Francisco was opened with its aid. Stationed at intervals along the coast-to-coast line, the mysterious bulb picked up the fading voice signal like a relay runner snatching the baton and passed it on to arrive at full volume three thousand miles away.

The audion tube had arrived, but only a few technical men knew what had happened or had the faintest glimmering of the giant role it was to play. The little tube was no self-advertiser. It didn't move, it made no noise, and it was hidden away where the public never saw it.

Its inventor did not share its modest traits. Recovering quickly from his ordeal in court, he blared the tube's merits with leather lungs. Armed with fresh funds, de Forest went on with his work. After fifteen years of semi-starvation, menial jobs, and heartaches, he had found the little key to the treasure house of electronics. It was also the key to colossal wealth, but for this purpose, de Forest could never quite make it fit. He knew a great deal about electricity, but not very much about finance, or about getting along with people.

Since early childhood, Lee de Forest was passionately involved in invention and gadget building, somewhat to the irritation of his father. The tall, deep-chested, bearded Reverend

Henry Swift de Forest, who was a proud descendant of a
Harlem burgher and who posed for photographs with his right
hand thrust into his frock coat like a bronze statue, always
assumed that Lee would enter the church. His mother, a descendant of the Mayflower's John Alden and the most beauti-
ful girl in her class at Grinnell College in Iowa, married her
pastor when she was choir leader of the Congregational Church
at Council Bluffs, Iowa. There Lee was born in 1873 in comfort and dignity. Both these boons were sacrificed when his
father, acting on high principle, accepted a poorly paid position as president of Talladega College in Alabama, which had
been founded by Northern missionaries for the education of
Negroes.

The de Forests were Yankees who considered Negroes their
equals, and as if that were not enough to condemn them, the
pastor and his sons were seen doing yard chores usually dele-
gated to blacks. So proper whites ignored the family, and the
neighbors' children were quick with insults and rocks. Lee
was kept to study, prayers and labor, and played only with
his brother and sister and a group of Negro children.

Yet the boy had resources. He had energy, imagination,
cocky arrogance, and a subscription to *Youth's Companion*,
with its wonderful diagrams and directions for building all
manner of fascinating devices. When there was no money for
Christmas toys, he and his Negro friends built crude model
railroad trains; on the Fourth of July they set off homemade
firecrackers filled with kerosene and gunpowder. Lee spent
long days on the floor plotting inventions on sheets of wrap-
ping paper and built batteries, compasses and primitive elec-

tric motors from the directions in his magazine. Downtown, he watched a printing press and asked the men how it worked; he crawled under a locomotive and figured out how the wheels were reversed. His delight was great when he found a blast furnace, and he built a model in his backyard that worked, after a fashion. He built an electroplating outfit and earned his first dollar replating a neighbor's silver. When he was thirteen he announced that he had solved the riddle of perpetual motion, long an impractical dream, by means of a combination of magnets, and marveled at his success when "illustrious philosophers" had failed.

At seventeen de Forest considered himself a professional inventor, but his father forced Latin and Greek upon him, held his devices worthless, and even burned some of them. Then the boy wrote his father a carefully phrased letter, beginning "Dear Sir," in which he tried to explain his ambitions and asked permission to prepare for the Sheffield Scientific Course at Yale. There followed a painful interview. "It is what I *must* do. It is my destiny," said the boy. He won.

Lee was sent to Mount Hermon School at Northfield, Massachusetts, chosen by his father because it was founded by the evangelist, Dwight L. Moody, to prepare for Yale. On the way to the station he saw a farm gate which could be opened and closed from the driver's seat by means of levers and recognized it as a copy of one of his own devices. This evidence that he could create things that people needed cheered him on his trip. At school he gorged himself eagerly on math and all the science courses available, and resented the required farm work which took him away from the laboratory. He did two years' work in one, graduated with honors, and easily passed the Yale entrance examinations. That summer, 1893, he managed to get to the Chicago World's Fair. He got a job pushing a tourist chair, and by urging all his fares to see the science exhibits, managed to spend most of his time examining machines and instruments that were new to him. He was fascinated by an electrical demonstration given by Nikola Tesla, and the gaunt Balkan became one of his heroes.

Lee de Forest was able to go to Yale because an early de Forest had endowed a slender scholarship open to students bearing the family name. He went to New Haven with head high and hand outstretched, and was disheartened and angry when he was ignored. Brash, scrawny, ill-dressed and with a rural Alabama accent, he envied his suave classmates and tried to make himself into his image of a "typical college man." Failing, he became a defiant lone wolf and a "greasy grind," as fervent students were once called. Many a Yale man who only meant to avoid a bumptious stranger made an unwitting contribution to the future of electronic communication. For now de Forest's inventive drive was intensified by a fierce desire to excel those who had snubbed him and to achieve wealth with which to buy ostentatious luxuries.

De Forest struggled to better his lot by turning out a long succession of inventions. He planned an airplane, a chainless bicycle, a "pants'-crease perpetuator," a typewriter, an improved smoking pipe, new drawing instruments, puzzles and optical illusions. He wrote short stories, essays and poems and was amazed when magazines like *The Century* returned them. When a New York transit firm offered fifty thousand dollars for an improved trolley car system, he worked nights for many weeks on a plan which he was sure would win the prize and was crushed when it attracted no notice. He devised a method for improving the efficiency of the steam engine and was enraged at the cool criticism of his physics teacher.

His great love was electricity. He feverishly studied the papers of Maxwell, Hertz, and other trail blazers. He also read Spencer, Huxley and Darwin and was torn with doubts about his father's fundamentalist faith. Living in solitary turmoil in a cold room on fifteen-cent meals, he finally collapsed and was sent to the infirmary, where he grimly consoled himself by reciting Henley's "I am the master of my fate. / I am the captain of my soul." Despite his many shortcomings, few men have made a better attempt at demonstrating that preposterous claim than Lee de Forest.

Cramming four years' work into three, he was graduated in 1896. He emerged from the ordeal of the class ballot with undisputed titles of "homeliest" and "nerviest," but was listed high in the "genius" category. Then his fortunes changed. His father died suddenly. His mother, who had always respected his gifts, decided that he should go to graduate school. To make this possible and to put his young brother through Yale, his mother opened a student rooming house in New Haven. Lee began to eat regularly, and he no longer was plagued by guilt for rejecting his father's literal interpretation of the Bible.

At that point Lee de Forest was struck by a bolt of intellectual lightning which served to focus his diffuse drives. He heard Professor Henry A. Bumstead lecture on Heinrich

Hertz's pioneer experiments with wireless waves. Hertz's discoveries were so recent that few teachers understood them, and few acts of communication have had a greater impact on the modern world than that lecture which one student was prepared to comprehend. Hertz, in 1887, was watching a device in his laboratory containing two spark gaps and observed a tiny discharge of energy which all his experience told him had no business there. What happened was that ultraviolet light, falling upon a piece of zinc, had broken the electric bonds which held some electrons in place and had knocked a procession of them out of their orbits. Since electrons are negative particles, they were attracted by the positive electrode of Hertz's apparatus. They leaped across the gap and set up the little stream of energy which he observed. This was the ancestor of today's photoelectric bulb, or "electric eye," since any kind of light, falling upon a suitable metal, sets up a small current which can be amplified to trigger a small motor for opening and closing doors, and other tasks of the sort.

Thomas Edison had also made a basic discovery in electronics which went almost unnoticed. In an attempt to prevent his early light bulbs from darkening because of deposits from his carbon filaments, he inserted a positively-charged plate in a bulb and found that a feeble but measurable negative current flowed from the filament to the plate. While Hertz discovered that light would "boil" electrons out of metal, Edison found that heat would do it, but he pushed the discovery aside and went on improving the light bulb.

Without foreseeing the practical implications of their work, Hertz and Edison had taken initial steps in the field later to be called "electronics." This word has sometimes been used incorrectly to include devices in which the current is confined to wires, but until recently its definition was basically simple: in an electronic device, current is liberated and passes through space to perform a function. Since the adoption of the transistor and its solid-state relatives, which behave differently, they have been included in the family of electronic devices.

De Forest studied the liberated current with passionate zeal, had vague intuitions about its future, and regretted Hertz's early death because he felt that the German scientist would have understood him. His thoughts turned to Tesla, then working in New York. He read all he could find about the great man's life and work, saved his money for months for a trip to the city, and carefully rehearsed a plea to work in his laboratory. Tesla received him and talked with him for an hour, but firmly, and probably wisely, refused to employ him. The combination would have been highly explosive.

Back in New Haven, de Forest began a series of messy experiments which irritated his teachers. He was denounced for driving nails in a fine new laboratory table. He was always blowing out fuses, and one night an auditorium went dark during a lecture. This was the last straw. He was asked to leave.

The war with Spain had just begun, so he enlisted, but peace came while he was still in training camp. He returned to Yale, where he was allowed to study for his Ph.D. Yale's great mathematical genius, Willard Gibbs, took an interest in him. Professor Gibbs's lectures were so profound that after thirty years of teaching he stated that perhaps six students had profited by them, but when de Forest needed a special course, he volunteered to conduct it for him alone. Soon de Forest won his doctorate. With a prospect of a job in Chicago, he borrowed fifty dollars and started for the station. Then his nerve failed. He returned to his old bench in the laboratory, put down his bag and set to work. Professor Bumstead found him there, gave him a fight talk, and pushed him out into the world.

In the fall of 1899 the erratic genius plunged into the long, harrowing grind which ended with the harnessing of the elusive electron. De Forest's career was full of minor failures, profitless side excursions, futile rages, a tempestuous romantic life, lawsuits, profligate splurges and interruptions caused by lack of funds. But however his trail meandered, through the years his steps drew nearer and nearer to the discovery of the little glass tube which became the key to the electronic age.

Dot-and-dash wireless was the sensation of the day, and the Italian scientist Guglielmo Marconi was its hero. But the best device then known to Marconi or to anyone else for picking these messages out of the air was a clumsy tube called the Branley coherer. It was full of metal filings which stuck together to form a circuit when a signal came in and then had to be tapped loose with a hammer before another signal could be detected. De Forest set out to invent a better detector.

Nominally, de Forest was an engineer in the telephone laboratory of the Western Electric Company in Chicago, but with the permission of a sympathetic superior, he was soon giving most of his time to his wireless device. Later he left for a job in Milwaukee at fifteen dollars a week, but was discharged when he refused to turn over his invention to his employer. Back in Chicago again, he subsisted on various small daytime jobs, and his real work began when he came home to his small bedroom, which was so cluttered with apparatus that there was hardly space for a cot.

One winter he was living on ten dollars a week earned by translating French technical papers. He went barefoot in his room to save his shoes, and penned a thoughtful memo in his diary that if he stood up as much as possible, his pants might last until spring. In testing various materials for use as electrodes, he began experimenting with silver. One Monday he inserted a silver dollar in his apparatus. On Thursday he got hungry and concluded that a half-dollar would do as well. The next day this shrank to a quarter, and on Saturday he was using a thin dime, which he caught himself eyeing ravenously. Before the day was over he had to stop work. He had eaten his electrode.

"Oh, the loneliness, the difficulties . . ." he wrote in his diary. "I am dwelling in a new realm. All in the dark. No precedents. No theory to guide. No apparatus. No co-workers. All things to be tried out and tested."

The tide soon turned. De Forest went to the Armour Institute and struck a bargain. He was to teach three hours a week in return for the use of the Institute's electrical laboratory. With the help of Edwin Smythe, a young telephone engineer who had caught his enthusiasm, de Forest finally completed his "responder," as he called it, an automatic detector of wireless telegraph signals which, although still crude and fallible, was a distinct advance over the tube of metal filings. At least it maintained a continuous circuit.

Highly excited, de Forest began outdoor distance tests. On a summer afternoon in 1901, with the rain coming down in sheets, he huddled beneath an unbrella on a hotel roof half a mile from the laboratory. He had put together an antenna made from metal barrel hoops and a lamp cord. Phones on his ears, he waited for the letter "h" which Smythe was to broadcast in Morse code. The message came through, loudly and distinctly. The next day they made a successful four-mile test. Then there was a five-mile test from a yacht in Lake Michigan.

De Forest was jubilant. Lipton's *Shamrock II* was soon to race the yacht *Columbia* off Sandy Hook, New Jersey. Borrowing carfare from Smythe, de Forest packed his apparatus and boarded a day coach for New York. He dashed from the station to the office of the Associated Press and proposed that he report the race by wireless from a tug. He was informed that the Associated Press had signed a contract for this service with the Marconi Company. But the Publishers' Press Association quickly signed up de Forest and agreed to furnish the tug. He was now in open competition with the famous and wealthy Marconi. In the few weeks before the race he had to rent a shop, buy materials and build his equipment. By great good fortune, he met a business man who advanced him a thousand dollars, so he founded the American Wireless Telegraph Company and began a day-and-night grind in preparation for the race. A few days before the event was scheduled, he collapsed from lack of sleep and proper food and was carried to a hospital. Dragging himself from his bed, de Forest finished the work, and on the morning of the race he set out in his boat to beat Marconi.

The result was a general fiasco. Wireless was new, and it didn't occur to either pioneer that it was necessary to use different wave lengths. So they jammed each other's signals. No wireless reports came through at all, and the papers got their news by wig-wag.

De Forest, undaunted, plunged into a promotion scheme to finance his new firm. With holes in his shoes and hunger gnawing him, he lived in his dream of a world covered with wireless networks, and he talked in terms of millions. Money soon poured in, and de Forest's name was on every tongue. In 1903 the *Providence Journal* hired him to set up a wireless telegraph station on Block Island to give the paper up-to-the-minute news. This was so successful that the Navy engaged him to report maneuvers by wireless. Then he was called to England, where he pioneered in establishing wireless service between Wales and Ireland. He set up a station at Shantung, China, from which the Russo-Japanese naval war was reported. His demonstration at the World's Fair at St. Louis captured the imagination of the country. Then came a great triumph when the U. S. Navy awarded the de Forest company contracts to build five stations in Florida and the Caribbean area. But before the work was done, his company got into a serious financial jam. Its promotion schemes were too ambitious. De Forest's wireless telegraph period was over. He left the firm, taking with him only a thousand dollars in cash and the rights to an incomplete invention later known as the audion tube, which he believed had a future in sending voices over the air. His partners turned this invention over to him without question, for they considered the device worthless!

For years Lee de Forest had been fumbling with an elusive and daring idea. It all began with the curious behavior of a gas flame one September night in 1900 in the bedroom in Chicago. Working over one of his early wireless signal detectors, he was operating the transmitter when he noticed that the light on the wall brightened and dimmed in response to the sparking of the coil. He jumped to the conclusion that the flame of the gas lamp was detecting the wireless signals. He ran across the street to Smythe's room, hauled him out of bed, and told him the news. The two men stayed up all night, operating the transmitter in various rhythms and noting the instantaneous response of the gas light. Here, it seemed, was a clue to a new device for receiving air waves. Their hopes were dashed when they placed the transmitter in another room and found that the light no longer fluctuated. It was the vibration of the transmitter, not the wireless waves, which had disturbed the flame within the gas mantle. Yet de Forest clung to the notion that heated gases could be used to detect electric waves. This led him to numerous experiments. Many of them were based on false ideas, but they brought him nearer and nearer to his unforeseen goal.

His next step was to place a gas flame between two electrical terminals. This arrangement showed some promise as a detector of air-wave signals, but drafts ruined reception, so he put a glass container over the device. From this he went on to a gas-filled bulb with a flame to heat it. Then he abandoned the flame and built a kind of light bulb with an added plate, separated from the filament by a short gap—similar in principle to Edison's forgotten experimental bulb. This two-element tube, or "diode," as it is called, was an improvement over previous detectors, and de Forest's hopes were high, but J. A. Fleming of England had patented a similar tube the year before, and de Forest lost out in infringement proceedings.

He set out to build a better receiving tube. He was then working in an attic laboratory in the Parker Building, which later burned, on the corner of Fourth Avenue and Nineteenth Street, New York. There is a brass plaque bearing his name on the building which now stands on the site, for it was there that he invented the audion, or amplifying tube. He did not do this swiftly or surely. An onlooker with prophetic vision would have broken out in a cold sweat as de Forest fiddled and fumbled, first testing bits of tinfoil and strips of metal in various positions, and would have finally collapsed with relief as the inventor twisted a piece of platinum wire into a design roughly resembling a kitchen grid and inserted it in the bulb between the filament and the plate.

This epochal event took place at about midnight on New Year's Eve, 1906. De Forest and Frank E. Butler, an assistant, had spent the evening directing the construction of the tubes in the shop of a Mr. McCandless, a maker of Christmas-tree bulbs, on Fourteenth Street. When two tubes were finished, they packed them in cotton in an old shoe box and ran back through heavy rain to the laboratory. While horns and sirens rent the night, they plugged in the first tube. There was a flash of light as it burned out. They inserted the second tube. It lasted thirty minutes, long enough for them to speak before a transmitter in the next room and receive clear messages of surprising volume. More tubes were made, and many tests followed. The late John V. L. Hogan, a de Forest assistant who was later to become director of New York's famous high-fidelity station WQXR and inventor of a method for sending pictures over radio waves, used to stand over the transmitter muttering a political slogan of the day, "Reciprocity Forever," while de Forest, earphones in place, cheered with delight as the wonderful words came to him through the world's first amplifying tube.

De Forest did not know at first that he had discovered an amplifier. He thought he had designed a superior detector—a great accomplishment in itself. It was a crude device, and many improvements were made by other scientists. The gas in the tube turned out to be a handicap, and when the tube was pumped out to obtain a high vacuum, performance was greatly improved. Several years passed before de Forest or anyone else knew how it worked or understood its true function and value.

The grid—the heart of the device—has been compared to a Venetian blind. By manipulating the controlling cords of such a blind at your window, you can alter the sunlight pattern on the floor, and you could even work out a clumsy communication code in this manner. De Forest's electronic blind works a million times as fast and is far more accurate in its control. The lead from the radio aerial is connected to the grid, and the tiny amount of energy which comes through the air from the radio station "pulls the cords" of this "blind" to increase or diminish the flow of electrons through the tube. Thus the feeble radio signals impress their pattern upon the much greater current which flows through the tube from the household light socket. Vastly more powerful than the original stimulus, but reshaped by the grid in its sound-carrying mold, the current can now operate the loud-speaker. By hooking up several audion tubes in a series, so that the increased output of the first tube operates the grid of the second tube, and so on, any amount of amplification can be obtained. For instance in a small radio, four tubes, each the size of a little finger, can multiply the power of an incoming radio signal twenty-five billion times between the aerial and the loud-speaker. Even the infinitesimal currents in the human brain and nerve centers can be made audible by means of this electronic tool.

Since then the principle of the little glass tube has been used to construct a vast array of electronic devices. More hurdles have been placed in the tube to guide the acrobatic electrons in varied jobs both delicate and powerful. Many of these complicated devices have no outward resemblance whatever to the audion tube which sired them. When de Forest inserted the bent wire between the filament and the plate, he found that two and one equaled many times three, and since then his discovery has been compounded to astronomical figures. Today, the tiny metal transistor performs many of the functions of the electron tube, but for many important uses the descendants of de Forest's tube are still essential and probably always will be.

Dreaming of riches, the thirty-three-year-old inventor promptly organized the de Forest Radio Telephone Company to manufacture his new tube and to develop radio telephony. This move aroused little public interest, for a number of new wireless developments, notably the invention of the crystal detector with its "cat's whisker," later used by millions of radio amateurs, competed for attention.

The new tube was not ready for use, and he had not yet found out that it could be made to "oscillate," or generate high-frequency currents for transmitting voice signals as well as for receiving and amplifying them. So with his tireless passion for experimentation, he contrived another crude sending device. The result was an unexpected public triumph.

On a sunny spring morning in 1907, a young wireless operator named Arthur Wallis sat half asleep in the radio shack at the Brooklyn Navy Yard, according to the account of T. R. Kennedy, Jr., retired electronics expert of *The New York Times*. An occasional dot-dash message came in. Birds were singing, and music from a hurdy-gurdy came through the window. Then a brisk new theme entered the soothing concert —strains from the overture to *William Tell*. Wallis leaped up, thinking he had been dreaming. The music seemed to come from within the room. He put on his earphones. Incredibly, the music seemed to spring from them. Suspecting a hoax, he searched the room for a concealed phonograph. He shouted for his chief and phoned the officer of the day. Then someone recalled that on Chirstmas Eve, 1906, the radio pioneer Reginald Fessenden had transmitted music and voices to ships at sea from his station at Brant Rock, Massachusetts. What they heard in Brooklyn, according to radio historians, was the first such transmission in New York.

The music came from a phonograph in de Forest's laboratory about four miles away. All previous transmissions had been limited to a distance of a few feet inside the laboratory; now de Forest, Hogan and Butler rigged up a device called a "singing arc light," which they thought would generate wireless waves. Voice transmission to the next room was successful, then de Forest got another idea.

"Let's hang a wire to the flagpole on the roof," he suggested, "and run a lead to the transmitter. Maybe we can get our signals out a little way; perhaps someone will hear us. We won't try to reach anyone in particular; we'll just let 'er go free. We'll *broadcast* it."

The musical program was an afterthought. Their voices were tired from testing, so they used the phonograph. It was not until they saw the papers the next morning that they knew anyone had heard them. The Navy had reported the strange event. Soon reporters came to the laboratory, de Forest's hit-or-miss experiment became a world-wide sensation, and his word "broadcast" entered the language. Thirty-four years later the anniversary was observed on a network program in which de Forest, speaking from Los Angeles, exchanged recollections of the great day with Butler, speaking from New York. The anniversary broadcast and its reception were made possible by millions of audion tubes, sophisticated descendants of the crude glass bulb which lay in its shoe box that day in 1907.

After the 1907 broadcast, de Forest was widely known as

an eccentric genius who made almost incredible predictions about the future of wireless. He had a loyal following among young radio amateurs who were building sets and exchanging messages, but investors were cautious. For one thing, critics said, radio-telephony afforded no privacy, and was therefore impractical. His plans for broadcasting news and entertainment for everyone were considered flamboyant. Still living precariously, he snatched at every chance to demonstrate his wireless equipment. There was a regatta on Lake Erie that summer, and Commodore W. R. Huntington of the Sandusky, Ohio, Yacht Club invited de Forest to install his radio-telephone on his fine cruiser yacht, the *Thelma*, and report the progress of the races to a shore station. De Forest and Butler set up their station in the wheel house, but since the *Thelma* was a wooden ship, had trouble obtaining a good "ground." They solved the problem in the owner's absence by nailing large sheets of copper to her mahogany hull. Stunned when he saw the desecration, Huntington recovered and complimented them on their ingenuity. The race bulletins were a success, but the yacht was never quite the same again.

More demonstrations followed. De Forest predicted "wireless opera," and with the cooperation of the Metropolitan Opera Company, broadcast *Cavalleria Rusticana* with Caruso in the leading role. A few hundred people heard the performance, but reception was so poor that he won few converts.

Businessmen conceded that he had an interesting gadget, but asked him what practical use it could be put to. "What is the use," de Forest replied in a letter to *The New York World*, "of speaking across hundreds or thousands of miles? What is the use of listening in your own home to the melodies of master musicians played in some distant auditorium? What is the use when some distant mariner, fog-bound and lost . . . can call to a listener on the nearest shore and hear in a still, small voice his name repeated and his whereabouts disclosed? . . . Or when the admiral, on his bridge, can give his orders direct, *viva voce* to all or any of the commanders of his widely scattered squadron?"

Perhaps the last example reached the ears of Admiral Robley D. ("Fighting Bob") Evans of the U. S. Navy, who became a militant advocate of de Forest's radio-telephone, predicting that it would become a necessity on every war vessel in the fleet. As a result, the Navy became the chief customer of de Forest's company. In the late fall of 1907, when the United States Fleet made its historic cruise around the world, more than twenty vessels were equipped with de Forest's radio-telephones. From the vantage point of today's knowledge of radio, it is not surprising that these early sets were not very reliable, but once during the cruise they were of great value in a storm when other means of communication were useless. A few prophets caught a glimpse of their future. The exact date of the first practical use of the audion tube, both for sending and receiving, is in some doubt, but soon the little grid which de Forest inserted became the key to radio and long-distance telephone communication the world over.

The Navy contract spurred the sale of the de Forest company's stock. Capitalists shunned it, but de Forest's associates beat the drum with vigor and sold thousands of shares to small investors. The stock was a poor risk.

Wrote Gleason L. Archer in his *History of Radio:* "In discussing the phenomenon of public indifference to the marvellous invention of radio, which from 1906 to 1920 was virtually unknown in America, Owen D. Young, [then Chairman of the Board of the General Electric Company] in a conversation with the author on February 5, 1937, expressed opinion that this was the fate of nearly every great invention.

" 'Fifteen years is about the average period of probation,' he declared, 'and during that time the inventor, the promoter and the investor who see a great future for the invention generally lose their shirts. . . That is why the wise capitalist keeps out of exploiting new inventions and comes in only when the public is ready for mass demand.' "

When de Forest and his associates were brought to court in 1913 for the historic trial, the Government presented voluminous evidence to show that the condition of the company and the prospects of radio-telephony had been falsely represented for the purpose of selling stock. In defense, de Forest took the stand and told the story of his struggles, which won him sympathy. His attorney stressed the fact that he was a scientist with little knowledge of finance. Yet he was a director and a large stockholder, and one should not condemn too harshly the prosecutor who tried to send him to prison.

To shift focus from the inventor to the man, Lee de Forest met a girl in 1907 who lived with her mother across the hall in his New York apartment house. The mother, Mrs. Harriet Stanton Blatch, was the daughter of Elizabeth Cady Stanton, the suffragette, and the daughter, Nora, was named for the independent "new woman" of Ibsen's play *The Doll's*

House. Nora had an engineering degree from Cornell and played the piano. Both accomplishments appealed to de Forest. They fell deeply in love, and although they met every day, he wrote to her every night. To understand his work, she studied electrical engineering, and soon they were married. They went to Europe on their wedding trip, where he made a broadcast from the Eiffel Tower containing a plea for votes for women. Nora worked with her husband in his laboratory for a time, then a daughter was born. Later their marriage became a battle between two strong personalities and ended in divorce. Years later at a New York theater he met Mary Mayo, a pretty singer, and fell instantly in love. They married and lived happily for a time in California, where he took a modest job when his fortunes were low. Later they parted. Finally in 1930 he married Marie Mosquini, a motion picture comedienne whom he met at a California beach party. She adjusted herself to his mercurial moods and pampered him for the rest of his life.

Since his student days, de Forest had always pined for the trappings of wealth. Once when temporarily rich he built an ornate house with gardens and fountains in Spuyten Duyvil, New York, overlooking the Hudson, and called it "Riverlure —Where Dreams Come True." He lost his money and the dream vanished. Years later he rented a sumptuous chateau, with ten servants, near Monte Carlo and thought of settling on the Riviera. At seventy he planned another "dream house" on a California mountain top, to be built when he sold another invention.

Whether he lived in a garret or a palace, he never stopped

working, and sometimes he deserted guests without a word
when a new idea came to him. Once when his hand was burned
by a live wire, he wondered if high-frequency waves could be
used as a "radio knife" for bloodless surgery. He "operated"
on raw beef and found that the waves sealed the capillaries,
preventing hemorrhage. Early surgical tests were abandoned,
but today his instrument has replaced the scalpel in many
delicate operations. In 1916, to demonstrate radio's uses, he
became the world's first disc jockey and newscaster, broadcasting nightly phonograph programs from the roof of his
Highbridge, New York, factory. That year he broadcast the
Harvard-Yale game, and on election night committed the
world's first radio boner, announcing, as the newspapers did,
the election of Hughes to the Presidency.

In the twenties, de Forest spent several years of hard work
and an estimated $185,000 on a talking-picture invention
called Phonofilm. Stars like Eddie Cantor, George Jessel and
Weber and Fields, as well as Presidential candidates, were
seen and heard in motion picture theaters by means of the
de Forest system. While he was negotiating for its sale, War-
ner Brothers, Hollywood producers, selected the competing
Vitaphone talking picture process, and the de Forest invention
became worthless. An essential item of the Vitaphone system
was de Forest's audion tube, but he had parted with all rights
to his greatest invention years earlier.

De Forest won and lost four fortunes in his stormy career,
which wound through a complex maze of legal and financial
thickets. In 1913, when he badly needed money, he sold the
wire telephone rights to his audion tube to the American

Telephone and Telegraph Company for fifty thousand dollars, a ridiculously low sum. Larger payments came later for other rights, but he was always an improvident plunger. In 1933 when Radio City, hailed as a monument to the electronic arts, was dedicated, he was penniless and jobless. Three years later he filed a petition for bankruptcy, listing four hundred dollars in assets.

De Forest was sixty at the time, but rebounded with amazing resilience, his blue eyes still sparkling, his laugh ready, and his diction as pungent as ever. He secured fresh capital and opened a plant in Pasadena, California, for the manufacture of diathermy machines for medical use. Marie discharged the servants and took over the kitchen, and the venture became a modest success. In vigorous health, he hiked twenty miles every Sunday and for many years observed his birthday by climbing a mountain. During his final years he was in great demand as a speaker at dinners held by radio groups. Peppery to the last, he savagely attacked broadcasters for the quality of the programs he had made possible. Surrounded by plaques and citations, he died on June 30, 1961, honored throughout the world as the father of radio.

CHAPTER NINE

IGOR SIKORSKY

Maestro of the Spiral Wing

In the early 1940's, residents of western Connecticut often stopped to gaze skyward as an awkward, bumbling craft which looked something like a praying mantis beat its way through the air. The odd ship didn't care how slow it went, or in what direction. It would back up, go sidewise like a crab, fly cater-cornered or up or down. It would stop in its tracks at the pilot's wish. Equipped with pontoons, it would alight on land or water, and unlike other aircraft, it would take off vertically with no forward run. Those who rode in it experienced a completely new sensation of locomotion. Some reported that it was like riding an amiable old plow horse.

This was the American public's introduction to the helicopter, a name derived from the two Greek words *helix*
(spiral) and *pteron* (wing) and pronounced "hellicopter,"
not "heelicopter." Its rescue devices, then new, were to save
thousands from sinking ships, arctic wastes and flooded
houses. Known in the Korean War as the "infuriated palm
tree," it became an angel of mercy to downed airmen, winging
its way over pathless rugged terrain and dipping to ground on
hilltops and in clearings where no other type of aircraft could
land. It was to be used to spray crops, patrol pipe lines, stock
streams, service lighthouses, take pictures, survey traffic, lift
cargo, take people to airports and round up buffalo. More
uses for the ungainly craft are found every year. The languid
beat of the whirlybird's floppy wings is now a sight so common
that it is hard to believe that as a practical flying machine
it is only about twenty years old.

Sometimes these early craft were flown by their inventor,
the shortish, gray-mustached scholarly Igor Ivanovitch Sikorsky, but more likely he was working in his plant at Stratford,
Connecticut, on improvements of his primitive ship. Many
men have created helicopters of many types, but Sikorsky,
one of the world's greatest aviation pioneers in both fixed-
wing and rotary aircraft, designed and built the first working
helicopter in the Western Hemisphere and has doubtless contributed more to the craft's development than any other inventor in its history.

When a visitor entered Mr. Sikorsky's office, he rose and
bowed in a European manner. The visitor had his full attention. Speaking in a slightly foreign accent, he outlined the

early development, the problems, and the possibilities of the helicopter in vivid, explicit, carefully framed statements that could be printed with no changes. When speaking of complicated engineering matters, he effortlessly translated technical terms into language a bright junior-high student, a congressman, or a writer could comprehend without strain. If a visitor thought he was receiving special consideration, he soon learned that Mr. Sikorsky treated everyone, from corporation presidents to mechanics, exactly the same. He was always precise, correct and unassuming, and men who have worked with him through the crises, disasters and frustrations of forty years have said that they have never once known him to raise his voice or fail in courtesy.

Such poise and urbanity are often evident in products of lifelong financial security and it would be easy to believe at first meeting that this man had never worried about paying the rent. But old fliers speak of the days "when Sikorsky was starving at Roosevelt Field," and a look into his past reveals, for instance, a White Russian emigré of thirty-one riding a New York subway to the end of the line and toting a borrowed slide projector through icy streets to some obscure suburban hall, there to lecture on astronomy for as little as three dollars. Someone once defined "guts"—a word Sikorsky would not use—as "grace under pressure." He always had that quality.

Igor Sikorsky was born in Kiev, Russia, in 1889. The son of an eminent professor of psychology who was a recognized authority in mental diseases and the author of many books, the boy was steeped in science when he was very young. His father took him on vacation hikes and talked to him about electricity, astronomy and physics. Too frail as a boy for rugged games, he turned to invention. He built several batteries, a small electric motor and a steam-powered motorcycle. He found a radical pamphlet giving directions for making a bomb from materials which could be bought at retail stores, and he set off small explosions in the garden until neighbors complained.

His interest in flying began when his mother, who had studied medicine and was a great admirer of Leonardo da Vinci, showed him da Vinci's sketch of a proposed craft which resembled, in principle, the modern helicopter. He had a dream in which he was flying in a palatial skyship, and he talked about flying with anyone who would listen. He asked the opinion of many scientists who came to his father's house. They told him that according to competent authorities, human flight was impossible, since not even Nature could put a bird in the air weighing more than thirty pounds or so. He considered their statements a personal challenge and worked in his room on a model of a strange craft which he hoped would rise directly from the ground by means of an overhead propeller. Whittling out his propellers and using a twisted rubber band for power, he made several models that would not fly. Finally he made a ship that whirred through the air and smacked the ceiling.

The boy did creditably in school, but was never a star student. He hated to spend his time on subjects that did not appeal to him. In the Naval Academy at Petrograd, which he entered at fourteen, he liked the active duty on ships, but decided that he really wanted to be an engineer. After three years he resigned. Since educational programs in Russia were disrupted by the attempted revolution of 1905, he spent six profitable months in a private technical school in Paris. The next fall he entered the Polytechnic Institute of Kiev, where he conceived a distaste for theoretical studies and higher mathematics. His fingers itched for drills and wrenches, flying machines filled his daydreams, and he spent his spare time at his home workbench and drawing board.

A great, confident vision of the future of aviation, in which he had to play a part, came to Sikorsky in the summer of 1908, when he was nineteen. He and his father were spending one of their walking, reading vacations in the German mountains. In a small hotel he found an old newspaper in which he read for the first time a reliable and accurate account of the pioneer flight of the Wright brothers at Kitty Hawk five years before. He was amazed that the reporter, an eye witness of the event, apparently did not realize its world-wide importance.

"It surprised me not to see big editorials in the papers of the world," he wrote in his biography, *The Story of the Winged-S*, "declaring that the age-long dream of giving wings to man, a possibility that was predicted and expected by some and positively denied by others, finally had become a fact."

Two years before, Wilbur Wright had written: "Like all novices we began with the helicopter, but soon saw that it had no future and dropped it." The boy had not heard of that statement, but it probably would not have stopped him. He could not wait to return home. He bought materials and began experimental work on a real helicopter in his hotel room.

Building a four-foot propeller and using a weight and pulley to spin it, he tested its lifting power and concluded that with a bigger propeller and more power, a practical helicopter was possible. Back home in Kiev, he went on with the work after school hours and read everything on aviation he could find. Soon he felt ready to build a real machine, but when he looked into the costs of engines and parts, he was dismayed.

During this period of burgeoning ambition, only one person took his plan seriously. His older sister Olga ran a school for feeble-minded children in some upstairs rooms of the family house, and when Igor was weary from work, he went up and talked to her of his plans and frustrations. Now he gloomily told her of the impasse. Paris was the world's aviation capital, he explained. It was the only place to talk with fliers, study their machines, and buy an engine and proper materials. But Paris might as well be Mars. Olga listened sympathetically. Finally she spoke.

"I have saved up three thousand rubles," she said. "You take it. Go to Paris and buy your engine."

Relatives and friends shook their heads. The boy's schooling would suffer. Olga's savings would go down the drain. Paris was a gay city, no place for a boy alone with a large sum of money. But when the argument ended, Igor, with the three thousand rubles (about fifteen hundred dollars), boarded a train for the great adventure.

At the Paris airfields Sikorsky talked with pioneer zealots and eagerly watched them taxi their primitive crates down runways, sometimes skipping clumsily through the air like barnyard turkeys. He enrolled in a flying school which met in a hangar and had no examinations, diplomas or textbooks. After a few months he knew the little others knew, and "graduated."

"Don't waste your time on a helicopter—it's hopeless," his teacher told him when he said good-by. So Sikorsky bought a twenty-five horsepower motor and some parts and returned to Kiev to build a helicopter. He also resumed his studies at the Polytechnic Institute. His father let him transform one of the rooms of the house into a shop, and in the summer of 1909 he built his first weird machine and assembled it in the back yard. It had two lifting propellers mounted on the same vertical shaft and rotating in opposite directions. On his first test he ran into what is now recognized as a major problem of helicopter design—violent vibrations shook the craft. Using common sense and intuition, he cured the trouble. In a later test the machine tried to turn over and nearly wrecked itself. "That made me very happy," he recalls. "It seemed to me that it was trying to go into the air." Using scales to measure its lifting power, he found that it could not take off with a man on board, but he was not disheartened. He had learned a great deal that could not be found in books, so he dismantled the ship and eagerly drew up plans for a new one.

His father dipped into his savings from writing textbooks and staked the budding inventor to another trip to Paris and two more engines. To learn more about propeller design, Igor built two air-driven sleighs and tested a series of props made for him by a local carpenter. He finished his second helicopter the following spring. It almost lifted its own weight of four hundred pounds. He knew now that a practical helicopter

could be built. More power and differently designed propellers would do the trick. But the time had come to cast up
accounts. He had worked for a year and a half and had spent
a large sum of the family money with no tangible results.
Helicopter problems were complicated; the fixed-wing planes
he had seen in Paris were simple by comparison, and he had
already laid out plans for a small biplane. Reluctantly he
shelved his flying windmill and began a new career at the
age of twenty-one.

During the next two years Sikorsky built six planes in a
plant on the outskirts of Kiev, escaping miraculously from
numerous crashes. His helpers were Fursoff, a furniture re-
pairer; Ponasuk, a handyman; a local plumber; and several
schoolmates who worked for nothing. At the end of the day his
father's gardener arrived by streetcar with a hot meal. The
crew ate dinner, built a fire, and gazed for long hours at the
embers, reviewing their work and discussing the giant aircraft
that would some day girdle the globe.

The fifteen-horsepower motor of the first plane could barely
get it off the ground. A more powerful plane flew two hundred
yards, but landed heavily and cracked up. They rebuilt it
and it rose to eighty feet, but Sikorsky learned about air
pockets the hard way. He crashed in a ravine, wrecking the
plane completely. He crawled from the ruins and built a new
plane with a forty-horsepower motor and numerous improvements. It made several satisfactory flights, but Sikorsky was
not only learning how to build planes, he was teaching himself to be a pilot. Within a week the plane crashed through a
frozen pond, taking the inventor with it.

By this time Sikorsky was trailing his class at school, and the family bank account was rapidly dwindling. But with complete confidence and no reproaches, his father put a second mortgage on the house and told Igor to proceed. He built two more planes. The plumber made the radiators, a bicycle repair shop turned out the undercarriages, and with memories of bumps and bruises, Sikorsky added shock absorbers made from kitchen-door springs. The "S-5" justified his family's faith. In it Sikorsky made cross-country flights and won his pilot's license. Invited to take part in Army maneuvers, he flew for an hour at fifteen hundred feet and was presented to the Czar. Now becoming famous, he began to earn money giving exhibition flights. On one of these, his motor failed at a hundred and fifty feet. He picked the best landing spot, which happened to be a railroad yard. The plane turned over, but the damage was small. Taking down the engine, he found that a mosquito in the gasoline had plugged up the carburetor. That taught him a lesson: a plane should have more than one engine, in case of mosquitoes and other unforeseen difficulties.

Using everything he had learned, he drew up plans for a sixth plane with a hundred-horsepower motor, designed to outfly anything in the country. He and his crew of amateurs built the plane in three months. Its performance was sluggish, but after they tore it down and streamlined it, it flew at seventy miles an hour with the pilot and two passengers, breaking the world's record. Two months later the plane won the highest award in the Moscow aircraft exhibition, and Sikorsky had arrived. Just before his twenty-third birthday a big Petrograd firm bought exclusive rights to manufacture Sikorsky's planes and made him designer and chief engineer of the aircraft plant. Within two years he paid back the twenty-five thousand dollars his family had risked on his career. He was on his way toward making a fortune.

When Sikorsky arrived in Petrograd with his home-trained crew of aircraft builders, people who once said that human flight was impossible were now saying that no one could fly a plane weighing more than a ton. You had to stop somewhere, they said. But the young man from Kiev had fantastic plans for a huge craft with four motors and four propellers and a large enclosed cabin carrying a number of passengers. Skeptics "proved" that such a monstrosity would not rise from the ground, that if one of the motors should fail it would lose balance and crash, and that it was too big to make a safe landing. Sikorsky listened gravely and built the ship, the world's first four-motored plane. On a test flight, the "Grand," as they called it, remained aloft an hour and fifty-four minutes with eight passengers on board, a world's record. Czar Nicholas II came to see the plane and presented Sikorsky with a gold watch. After refuting critics by making more than fifty flights with no trouble, the plane was wrecked by a curious accident. While it was on the ground, an engine fell out of a rival's plane and smashed through it. This was a heavy blow to Sikorsky, but at least it was not his father's money, and the plane's performance was so impressive that the company quickly authorized an even larger one.

Sikorsky's new giant, finished in 1913, quickly became the wonder of the aviation world. It could carry sixteen passengers and had a heated, electric-lighted salon and a private stateroom with the first sleeping berth ever put in a plane. In front was an open-air balcony, or "bridge," where the captain could survey the weather like the skipper of a ship. The plane soon broke endurance records, but the inventor's greatest triumph came when he flew from St. Petersburg to Kiev, landed at the scene of his early fumbling trials, and took his father for his first plane ride.

When war broke out, Sikorsky converted to bombers and built seventy-five four-engined planes, which made hundreds of raids on German targets. Then, in 1917, came the Russian Revolution. After several of his friends were shot, Sikorsky abandoned his fortune of some five hundred thousand dollars, which was invested in real estate and government bonds, and escaped from Murmansk on a crowded English boat. After a brief stay in Paris, he sailed again and landed in New York in March, 1919, with six hundred dollars, no friends and little English, prepared to start again from scratch at the age of thirty.

Lodging in a six-dollar-a-week room and eating on eighty cents a day, Sikorsky frequented flying fields and wistfully watched the planes take off, but he couldn't get a job, for the warplane budget had been cut to the bone after the Armistice, and commercial aviation had not been born. His first break came from the prophetic General "Billy" Mitchell, who sent him to Dayton to design a super-bomber for the Army. The appropriation ran out after six weeks, and he was back in New York. Then he heard that a group of Russian immigrants on the lower East Side was looking for a mathematics teacher in night school, and he brushed up his algebra and got the job. As students learned of his background, he was asked to lecture on aviation and astronomy. This left his days free, and he set to work designing transport planes and looking for capital.

Sikorsky's predictions about the future of flying excited his students, many of whom were skilled workmen, and they offered to help him. Meetings were held and the hat was passed for sums as little as ten dollars. A Russian refugee who ran a farm near Roosevelt Field, Long Island, offered his back yard and outbuildings for a workshop. In the spring of 1923 the Sikorsky Aero Engineering Corporation was formed on less than a thousand dollars capital, and work was begun on a two-engine passenger plane. Michel and Serge Gluhareff, Russian glider inventors, and Michel Buivid, an engineer who was Sikorsky's schoolmate in Kiev, came to work for fifteen dollars a week. They bought a secondhand drill press for $1.80, made big shears from an old auto bumper for cutting aluminum, got angle irons from bedsprings in a junk yard, and bought other parts in five-and-ten-cent stores. When some of the makeshift parts wouldn't fit, Sikorsky redesigned the plane.

Cold weather came, their hands were too stiff for work, and the money ran out. Then Sikorsky's friend Serge Rachmaninoff, the composer, lent money to rent a leaky old hangar at Roosevelt Field. When it came time to make the fabric coverings for the wings, Sikorsky's sister Helen, who had married and moved to Long Island, volunteered with her sewing machine and sat up nights stitching the big sleeves, while her son Jimmy Viner, later Sikorsky's chief test pilot, carted the ma-

terial back and forth, swept out the hangar, and bought sand-
wiches for the workmen when the treasury permitted. For
twenty weeks no one was paid. Eating was a problem, and the
discovery of the American baked bean probably saved the
venture. That and the telephone. Reporters covering a story
at the field used the corporation phone, leaving dimes and
quarters which were converted at once into food. Buivid had
credit at a grocery store, and that helped. And when things
got desperate, Sikorsky could always pawn the Czar's watch.
That year he was married to a girl from his native land, who
gamely learned how to be the wife of a struggling inventor.
The plane was finished in the spring, and someone borrowed
gasoline for a test flight. With great enthusiasm, the gang
rolled the ship out and swarmed aboard. Before Sikorsky
could stop them, the cabin was crowded, and the men had
worked so hard he didn't have the heart to turn them out.
The overloaded plane took off, lost altitude, made a forced
landing and was badly smashed. The men were only scratched,
but for Sikorsky it looked once more like the end of the
road.

After some weeks, he rebounded, and as a last, forlorn hope,
he staged the only grandstand play of his career. He called a
meeting of the fifty-odd stockholders and friends, most of
them Russians, who still believed in him, locked the door,
put the key in his pocket, and announced that they would stay
there until they had put up twenty-five hundred dollars to re-
build the plane. Fighting for his future in aviation, he elo-
quently outlined his plans and asked them to trust him once
more. He got the money. The rebuilt S-29, which carried four-

teen passengers and cruised at a hundred miles per hour, performed beautifully and was an immediate success.

The S-29, said to be the first American twin-engined plane
able to fly on one motor, had a spectacular career and did much
to establish Sikorsky as a plane-builder. He piloted it himself
on hundreds of chartered flights for aviation fans, then sold it
to a stunt flier. Later it was rented for advertising jobs and was
seen throughout the country pulling a streamer which bore
the words "United Cigar Stores." After logging half a million
miles, the old plane ended its days disguised as a German
bomber in a Hollywood motion picture.

The triumph of the S-29 attracted ample new capital, the
company was reorganized, and eating became a routine habit
among Sikorsky's faithful Russians. But one more serious
catastrophe awaited him. In the summer of 1926, the French
pilot Réné Fonck decided to try for the Raymond Orteig Prize
of twenty-five thousand dollars for the first nonstop flight between New York and Paris—the prize Lindbergh won the
following spring—and his backers ordered from Sikorsky a
special three-motored plane. The ship was finished in August,
but it took weeks more to install equipment for the long hop.
Sikorsky advised more testing, but the days were getting
shorter, the publicity buildup was tremendous, and Fonck
and his commercial backers were eager. On a dark morning
in September, while crowds of onlookers jammed the field and
hampered action, Fonck tried to take off and failed to rise.
The plane crashed and burned beyond the end of the runway
in what has since been called "Sikorsky Gulch." This was the

most promising plane Sikorsky had ever built. Two crew members were killed. The old hangar was shrouded in gloom.

Lindbergh's flight the following spring rescued American commercial aviation, and Sikorsky soon hit his stride with his famous S-38 ten-seater amphibian, one of a series of flying boats of various sizes. Noted people bought them, among them John Hay Whitney, Joseph M. Patterson, Colonel Robert McCormick, and the explorer-lecturer couple the Martin Johnsons. The Johnsons took two Sikorsky ships to Africa, where they used them in making a film. Lindbergh flew an S-38, and the Prince of Wales rode in one. Pan American Airways placed big orders.

In his modern new plant at Bridgeport, Connecticut, Sikorsky built more than a hundred S-38's, which flew a total of twenty-five million miles, pioneering long-distance mail and passenger service throughout the Western Hemisphere. The Flying Clippers followed, and to all the world the name Sikorsky came to mean fast, luxurious overseas air travel. The firm had now become a branch of the United Aircraft Corporation, and Sikorsky, primarily an inventor, was now freed of much administrative work.

But the Flying Clippers had done too good a job, and more trouble loomed ahead for Sikorsky and his gifted, temperamental, urbane Russians. When he proved that his amphibians could cross oceans, their heavy hulls and pontoons became obsolete. The Depression arrived, rich people stopped buying planes, and competition among aircraft firms became intense. Other makers developed ocean-hopping, land-based planes, and United Aircraft became restive at supporting Sikorsky's fine plant, bursting with talent but with no planes to build.

Orders came to cut the staff, and many stories are told of Sikorsky's attempts to save the jobs of his loyal compatriots, many of whom had formed a White Russian colony in the Bridgeport area and were members of the local Orthodox Church, of which Sikorsky was a leading member. When Bridgeport's Community Grand Opera Company gave their annual performance, the quality of an aria usually depended on one of Sikorsky's Russians. When the Grand Duchess Marie visited the plant, workers rose from benches and the great lady held court. In this atmosphere the gentle, mystical Sikorsky was father and protector. If a man was dropped from one department, he somehow turned up in another so that his family would not suffer. Sikorsky labored valiantly to cut costs, but explained to corporation executives that these refugees had lost every possession, had repeatedly faced death, and could not be expected to be deeply concerned about the Depression.

The time came when the Sikorsky plant had to be closed down, and Eugene E. Wilson, then vice-president of United Aircraft, had the sad task of delivering the blow, which might mean the end of Sikorsky's career. He had been told at the meeting of the executive committee when the decision was made: "There's a pearl in that Russian caviar somewhere. See if you can save it." So Wilson tempered his news with the suggestion that United might consider financing any individual research program Sikorsky had in mind.

Sikorsky accepted the decision calmly. In his formal but

warm manner he expressed his thanks for United's unfailing consideration, then launched a little discourse on the history of flight.

He began with Sir Isaac Newton, who proved conclusively that human flight was impossible, then skipped to Kitty Hawk, where Newton was refuted. He dramatically summarized the entire history of aviation as a record of the repeated accomplishment of the "impossible." This led him to the helicopter.

"The helicopter," he said, "while admittedly radical, and possibly 'impossible,' is wholly rational. Like no other vehicle, it will operate without regard to prepared landing surfaces. Thus it will free us of the most serious handicap to progress imposed by fixed-wing aircraft—airport limitations. So important is this development to the future of society that it becomes our responsibility to undertake it, regardless of apparent complications. If the Sikorsky Company does not create this craft of the future, another will. And finally, unlike the airplane, the helicopter will be used not to destroy, but to save lives."

Sikorsky followed his eloquent plea with an estimate that by cutting corners, he and four veterans of his engineering staff could build a flight model for thirty thousand dollars. He was told to go ahead, and if he followed his usual custom, he called a formal staff meeting, announced the news, toasted the project with a glass of wine, then went home and worked all night over his drawing board, sipping black coffee from a tiny cup and listening to Brahms or Rachmaninoff. During this period he also had a hideaway cabin where he sometimes worked alone for three days, cooking his own simple meals.

Sikorsky had never abandoned the helicopter; he had only postponed the project. For many years he had kept on his office desk a toy with a tin propeller with which he demonstrated the rotary-wing principle. Many other men had built experimental helicopters, most of them with little success, and Sikorsky had the advantage of their experience. In 1907, the year before his boyhood attempt, craft of the sort were built by two Frenchmen, Paul Cornu and Louis Breguet. All designers faced the problem of how many rotors to use. A single rotor will pull the fuselage around if the twisting power is not neutralized by an additional mechanism. Cornu hit upon two rotors, mounted on outriggers, turning in opposite directions. This solution has an appealing symmetry and has been used by other designers, but Cornu could not achieve control and stability. Breguet's first craft had four rotors. He got it off the ground but could not control it. Like Sikorsky, he became famous as a designer of fixed-wing planes. Years later he returned to the helicopter and was more successful when he mounted two contrarotating propellers on the same shaft. He lifted the ship to five hundred feet and is said to have flown at fifty miles per hour—an important step in helicopter progress. He planned a big transoceanic craft, but it was never built. One of the most complicated craft was built by the eccentric Russian exile George de Bothezat at McCook Field under government contract in the early twenties. One model had eight propellers used for lifting, horizontal propulsion and control. It rose a few feet from the ground on several tests; then the project was abandoned. Another cumbersome monster, built by Marquis Patéras Pescara of Spain, had biplane-type rotor blades for lifting the craft, and a propeller in the nose for forward flight. The ship looked like a bevy of World War I airplanes fastened around an upright shaft. It actually got off the ground.

The first operational rotary-wing craft was the autogiro, or gyroplane, which at first glance looked like a helicopter, but performed differently. The overhead rotor was given a spin by the engine to shorten take-off. After that it rotated freely, and forward propulsion was furnished by a conventional propeller in the craft's nose. Invented by Juan de la Cierva of Spain in the early twenties and later produced by two American firms, it was adopted and successfully flown by the Army Air Corps in the late thirties. A great future was predicted for this craft, but it had limitations: it could not rise or land vertically, and it could not hover.

One true helicopter won its spurs before Sikorsky's. In 1937 Dr. Heinrich Focke of Germany stirred the world by demonstrating his ship in an indoor sports arena in Berlin. Later it made a flight of 143 miles and was reported to have reached an altitude of more than 11,000 feet. The craft had two overhead rotors, mounted on outriggers, which turned in different directions.

At least a dozen other types of rotary-wing craft would interest a student of the subject. It had already been proved that a helicopter would fly. Preceded by a confusing array of machines and theories, Sikorsky faced the task of building a craft that was simple, durable, safe and easy to fly. He already had firm ideas on the subject. "One rotor is enough," he said. "Two rotors are like two women in the kitchen. You might think they would do twice as much work, but the efficiency of each is lowered by thirty-five per cent."

Within a year after starting his assignment, Sikorsky rolled an ungainly contraption from the hangar and prepared to test it. Onlookers, accustomed to the sleek, clean lines of an airplane, gazed at the squat framework of pipes, housing a motor and topped by a drooping horizontal propeller, and called it "Igor's Nightmare." Only Sikorsky knew how it should work, and he had to learn to fly it. Associates recall his stocky figure, in a business suit and an upturned felt hat a little small for him, sitting upright at the controls, "looking," as one remarked, "as though he had an open textbook in one hand."

Riding this pioneer helicopter was like taming a bucking bronco. Helicopter controls are much more complicated than those of a plane. In a plane the wing's airfoil is so shaped that when the airstream strikes it, a vacuum is created above the wing and upward pressure below it. The combination of the two forces provides lift, so long as the plane goes fast enough, and the few moving parts make for a smooth ride. In Sikorsky's helicopter, lift is provided by the motor-driven horizontal blades, independent of forward motion of the craft. This enables it to hover. The method of achieving horizontal flight is more complicated. Putting it simply, this is done by tilting the whole rotor a little so that it pulls the craft in the direction desired. Then to keep the overhead rotor from turning the ship around, there is a small vertical tail rotor which counteracts this torque effect and also aids in steering.

These moving parts had to be coordinated in order to get smooth control and stability, and Sikorsky made many teeth-rattling flights. These were safer than fixed-wing test flights, for he could practice with a helicopter at a height of three feet. In the early flights the ship was tethered with a ball and chain. For two years Sikorsky tore down and rebuilt, and made longer and higher flights. He put floats on the ship and showed that it could land on water.

In May, 1941, he kept a ship in the air for more than an hour and a half, establishing a world endurance record. At last people understood the amazing versatility of a flying machine that could rise vertically, stand still in the air, skim treetops, and land almost anywhere. The Army ordered its first helicopter a year later, and the ship was flown from Bridgeport, Connecticut, to Wright Field, Ohio, for delivery, making the first cross-country helicopter flight in the Western Hemisphere.

The VS-300, as it was called, established Sikorsky in the rotary-wing field, and since then about thirty-five hundred bigger and faster Sikorsky helicopters have beaten the air with their lazy wings. Aided by his success, many other firms have produced excellent helicopters of many types. There was an amusing scene when the old VS-300 went to its final resting place—the Henry Ford Museum at Dearborn, Michigan. At a ceremony attended by a large crowd, Sikorsky climbed into his ship, flew to the stands, hovered before Henry Ford and made the ship curtsy like a circus pony, while he raised his hat and bowed.

Igor Sikorsky retired in 1957 but continued work as a consultant on the exciting new monsters his firm produces. Long ago he thought of the helicopter as an aerial crane for moving heavy cargoes over rugged, roadless terrain. Now it has become a workhorse of power line construction. It picks up poles, carries them over hills and streams, and lowers them carefully into prepared holes, delivers the crossarms for workmen to fasten in place, then strings the wires by means of winch lines. A Sikorsky "Skycrane," which can lift four tons, has picked up a truck-size container from a railroad flat car and gently lowered it to the deck of a freighter in the Hudson River. Another craft has carried and poured concrete on a construction job. An important future is predicted for even larger helicopters in logging, mining, bridge building, forestry, and the transport of heavy vehicles and equipment.

After his whirling craft became successful, Sikorsky found time to pursue many interests. He has watched stars in his own small observatory and has driven a tractor on his Connecticut farm. He has visited and photographed the world's largest volcanoes and hovered over Mexico's Paracutin in his own helicopter. As his four sons grew up, he followed his father's custom and took them for peripatetic lectures in Vermont forests.

Progress cannot be achieved by reason alone, Sikorsky has insisted. Influenced by the rural Orthodox priests in his family line, he has pondered matters of the spirit in solitude. He once made a pilgrimage to the Palestine desert where Christ is said to have fasted, and has written two tracts setting forth his religious philosophy. Artists and writers may possess the gift of seeing beyond the curtain of time, he has said, and has modestly suggested that engineers may share the gift. His life appears to have justified this conclusion.

SELECTED BIBLIOGRAPHY

Archer, Gleason L. *History of Radio to 1926*. New York: The American Historical Society, Inc., 1938.

Barker, Preston W. *Charles Goodyear, Connecticut Yankee and Rubber Pioneer*. Boston: G. L. Cabot, 1940.

Beckhard, Arthur J. *Electrical Genius, Nikola Tesla*. New York: Julian Messner, Inc., 1959.

Carneal, Georgette. *A Conqueror of Space*. Authorized biography of the life and work of Lee de Forest. New York: Horace Liveright, 1930.

Davenport, Thomas. Autobiographical notes and letters concerning the author's invention of the electric motor. In the handwriting of Emily Davenport, his wife. Original in the library of the Vermont Historical Society, Montpelier. Photostat copy in the Engineering Societies Library, New York. 1851.

Davenport, Walter Rice. *Thomas Davenport, the Brandon Blacksmith*. Montpelier: The Vermont Historical Society, 1929.

Davenport, Willard G. "Thomas Davenport," *Vermont Historical Gazetteer*, III (1877).

Diesel, Eugen. *Diesel, der Mensch, das Werk, das Schicksal*. Hamburg: Hanseatische Verlagsanstalt, 1937.

"Diesels on Wheels," *Fortune*, December, 1934.

Goodyear, Charles. *Gum-Elastic and its Varieties*. With an account of its application and uses and of the discovery of vulcanization. New Haven: published by the author, 1853.

Griglietta, C. (ed.). *Electromagnetism*. With a full description of Davenport's machines. Philadelphia: Carey and Hart, 1838.

Hellman, Geoffrey T. "The Winged-S," *The New Yorker*, XVI (April 10, 17, 1940), 22–26, 23–28.

Johnson, Melvin M., Jr., and Haven, Charles T. *Automatic Arms, Their History, Development and Use*. New York: William Morrow and Co., 1941.

Lake, Simon. *Submarine*. The Autobiography of Simon Lake as told to Herbert Corey. New York: D. Appleton-Century Co., 1938.

———. *The Submarine in War and Peace*. Philadelphia: J. B. Lippincott Co., 1918.

Longstaff, Frederick V. *The Book of the Machine Gun*. London: H. Rees, Ltd., 1917.

Lubell, Samuel. "Magnificent Failure," *Saturday Evening Post*, CCXIV (January 17, 24, 31, 1942), 9–11, 20–21, 27.

Manchester, Harland: "The Great Diesel Boom," *Harper's*, CLXXXI (July, 1940), 196–203.

Maxim, Hiram Percy. *A Genius in the Family*. New York: Harper and Brothers, 1936.

Maxim, Sir Hiram Stevens. *Artificial and Natural Flight*. New York: Whittaker and Co., 1908.

———. *My Life*. London: Methuen and Co., Ltd., 1915.

Maxim, Hudson. *Hudson Maxim, Reminiscences and Comments*. As reported to Clifton Johnson. New York: Doubleday, Page and Co., 1924.

Morris, Charles Lester. *Pioneering the Helicopter*. New York: McGraw-Hill Book Co., Inc., 1945.

Mosenthal, Henry de. "The Inventor of Dynamite," *Nineteenth Century*, XLIV (October, 1898), 567–581.

———. "The Life Work of Alfred Nobel," *Journal of the Society of Chemical Industries*, May 31, 1899.

O'Neil, John J. *Prodigal Genius, Nikola Tesla*. New York: Ives Washburn, Inc., 1944.

Pierce, Bradford K. *Trials of an Inventor*. Life and discoveries of Charles Goodyear. New York: Carlton and Porter, 1866.

Pope, Franklin L. "The Inventors of the Electric Motor, with special reference to the work of Thomas Davenport," *The Electric Engineer*, January 7, 14, 21, 28, February 4, 1891).

Sikorsky, Igor Ivanovitch. *The Story of the Winged-S*. New York: Dodd, Mead and Co., 1944.

Silliman, Professor Benjamin. "Notice of the Electro-Magnetic Machine of Thomas Davenport," American Journal of Science and Arts, X, No. 1 (April, 1837).

Sohlman, Ragnar, and Schück, Henrik. *Nobel, Dynamite and Peace*. New York: Cosmopolitan Book Corporation, 1929.

Suttner, Bertha von. *Memoirs*. Boston: Ginn and Co., 1910.

Tesla, Nikola. "My Inventions," Electrical Experimenter, February–June, October, 1919.

———. "Some Personal Recollections," Scientific American, CXII (June 5, 1915), 537.

———. "The Problem of Increasing Human Energy," *Century*, LXIX (June, 1900), 175–211.

Van Gelder, A. P., and Schlatter, Hugo. *History of the Explosives Industry in America*. New York: Columbia University Press, 1927.

Wolf, Howard and Ralph. *Rubber, a Story of Glory and Greed*. New York: Covici Friede, 1936.

Wolf, Ralph F. *India Rubber Man*. Caldwell, Idaho: Caxton Printers, Ltd., 1939.

INDEX

211